OH, THE PLACES TO KNOW:
A Guide to Greenwich for Kids

Written and Published by **Rachel Khanna**

Enjoy !

Ellen Moshe

203 - 570 - 0275

Dedication

For my daughters: Kieran, Anjali, Sophie and Aaliya,
who unwittingly became my research assistants!

Published in 2007 by RACHEL KHANNA Publishing.

Copy editing by Erin Clermont.
Design by Teresa Fernandes, TFD STUDIO.
Illustrated by Michael Sloan, michaelsloan.com.

Second edition.

Printed in the United States.

ISBN: 0977956814

Library of Congress Control Number: 2007900807

PUBLISHER'S NOTE:
Neither the author nor publisher has any interest, financial or
personal, in the locations listed in this book. No fees were paid
or services rendered for inclusion in this book. While every effort
was made to ensure that information regarding phone numbers,
websites, hours of operation was accurate at the time of
publication, it is always best to call ahead to verify. Furthermore,
readers should consult with their medical practitioner before
acting on all health-related issues.

Contents

continued ☞

Contents continued

For those of you who did not see the prior edition of this book, this book started in 2000, when my husband and I found out we were expecting twins. We realized that we could no longer live in New York City and thus made the move to Greenwich. When we were looking for a house, I was lucky enough to find a real estate agent who had three children of her own and knew absolutely everything about what was going on in town for kids. Plus, she was more than happy to share her knowledge with me. There was so much to learn that I began thinking it might be helpful to put all that information in one place. So I got to work. I documented everything I had learned and later learned about resources for kids in Greenwich.

And here is the result. For new parents, or parents who are new in town, I've written a complete guide to everything you'll need to know to make your kids' lives – and your own – a lot easier in Greenwich. There has not been a day when I've regretted our decision to move here – Greenwich is quite simply a wonderful town in which to bring up children.

I would like to thank my husband, Jaideep, for his ongoing support; my four children, Kieran, Anjali, Sophie and Aaliya, who are my most active marketers of this book! I would also like to thank Susan Khanna, Cynthia Chang-Scanlan, Ruth Anapol, Marie-France Kern, Teresa Fernandes, Naomi Newman, Mari Vasan, Patty Dhar, Debi Bhandari, Gabriella Glaser - who have helped me promote the book, or given me new ideas for the book.

Finally, in working on the second edition of this book, I realized how quickly things change. While I have tried my hardest to ensure that all the information is accurate and up-to-date, information does change. So, if there is a listing which is incorrect or missing, please e-mail me at rachkhanna@gmail.com. I will be sure to include it in the next edition!

-Rachel Khanna

Chapter 1

YOUR CHILD'S HEALTH

My husband and I joke that I have no recollection of anything said or done during any of my pregnancies or in the six months after giving birth. So, if I have any advice, it's *plan ahead*—get as much rest as possible before the baby comes! True, giving birth provides the most amazing and exciting moments of your life, but it's also extremely tiring. Thus, planning ahead means understanding your options for childbirth and child care. Each family's needs are different, but knowing your options will help you understand how best to meet those needs. With my first child, I made every possible mistake a new mom could make: I worked until the day before I delivered; I refused painkillers for most of the night I was in labor, and therefore got not a wink of sleep; I chose to have the baby in the room with me during my stay at the hospital; and I allowed an endless stream of visitors. Needless to say, I was worn out by the time I got home—and after that didn't get any serious rest for the next six months! If this is not your first child, then getting rest before or after the baby comes is not necessarily an option... be ready to let things slide until you get your life back together. Just remember, you won't be getting any rest for the next 18 years!

HOSPITALS

Where you deliver your child is primarily a function of which hospital your obstetrician is affiliated with, but if there's any choice involved for you, the area offers some excellent choices:

GREENWICH HOSPITAL
5 Perryridge Road
Greenwich, CT 06830
Main Number: (203) 863-3000
Childbirth Education: (203) 863-3655
www.greenhosp.org

In addition to delivering your baby, Greenwich Hospital offers several programs for new moms and children through their **Tender Beginnings** program, such as:

Play Groups. When you deliver your child at Greenwich Hospital, you will be introduced to parents who had children around the same time as you did. This is a perfect way to meet parents with children the same age as yours. Many parents find new best friends through their babies in a play group. Moreover, the play groups are also open to parents who have just adopted babies.

Parents Exchange. This is a community program for parents with infants, toddlers, young children, or teenagers. Peer groups are organized and each group generates its own discussion topics. A child development professional is present to facilitate and guide discussion. For information about Parents Exchange, call (203) 863-3794.

Greenwich Hospital has many other programs to help you prepare for and take care of your baby.

STAMFORD HOSPITAL
30 Shelburne Road
Stamford, CT 06902
(203) 325-7000
(203) 276-1000
www.stamfordhospital.org

I delivered my fourth child at Stamford Hospital and was pleasantly surprised. The facilities are new and cheery—equal to the excellent maternity ward at Greenwich Hospital.

PEDIATRICIANS

Before giving birth, it's wise to decide on a pediatrician. Ask your obstetrician, close friends, or the nurses at the hospital where you will be delivering your child for recommendations. Some things to bear in mind when choosing a pediatrician:

Location. With a newborn, you'll be visiting your pediatrician often. In my experience, from October through April, one of my children will invariably have a runny nose, or worse, which requires a doctor. So pick one who's not too far away.

Personality. How do you like the doctor? If he or she is in a group practice, are you willing to visit other doctors in the group? Do you like them, too?

Efficiency. Waiting time and how emergency or non-emergency calls are handled are other important factors to consider when determining your choice of pediatrician.

CHILDREN'S MEDICAL GROUP OF GREENWICH
42 Sherwood Place
Greenwich, CT 06830

(203) 661-2440
Friends who frequent the Children's Medical Group are very pleased with the practice. And it's convenient to the center of Greenwich.

GREENWICH PEDIATRIC ASSOCIATES
8 West End Avenue
Old Greenwich, CT 06870
(203) 637-3212
Greenwich Pediatric Associates is a group of about seven doctors. They have been around for many years. In fact, I have met a number of Greenwich residents who were patients of Dr. Lewis when they were kids (he is still there).

NEXT GENERATION PEDIATRICS, LLC
Erik Cohen, M.D.
57 Old Post Road #2
Greenwich, CT 06830
(203) 661-6430

PEDIATRIC ASSOCIATES, P.C.
12 Rye Ridge Plaza
Rye Brook Plaza, NY 10573
(914) 251-1100
I take my children to this office and really like the doctors there. They are very attentive – my children had a 45-minute check-up recently – and the office is very nice.

RIVERSIDE PEDIATRICS, LLP
35 River Road
Cos Cob, CT 06807
(203) 629-5800
www.riversidepediatrics.com

I have heard good things about another pediatric group, in Stamford:

STAMFORD PEDIATRIC ASSOCIATES, PC
1275 Summer Street
Stamford, CT 06902
(203) 324-4109

DENTISTS

If you're looking for a pediatric dentist for your children, there are these choices:

DRS. ANGELO MILAZZO, IRENE BLOCK, VICTOR A. PARDI
1212 East Putnam Avenue
Riverside, CT 06878
(203) 698-0794
They also have an office at:
125 Strawberry Hill Avenue
Stamford, CT 06907
Within this practice, Dr. Pardi is an orthodontist.

OLD GREENWICH DENTAL ASSOCIATES
Dr. G. Busch, D.D.S., M.P.H.
182 Sound Beach Avenue
Old Greenwich, CT 06870
(203) 637-0665
www.oldgreenwichdental.com

DENTAL CARE KIDS
1500 Summer Street
Stamford, CT 06905
(203) 324-6171
www.DentalCareKids.com

DENTISTRY FOR CHILDREN, TEENS AND SPECIAL NEEDS PATIENTS
Michael S. Wolfman, D.M.D.
Hiroshi Tsuyuki, D.D.S.
149 East Avenue
Norwalk, CT 06851
(203) 838-4191

DR. MANTZIKOS
Orthodontist
279 Sound Beach Avenue
Old Greenwich, CT 06870
(203) 637-2027

DR. GARRICK F. WONG, DMD
Orthodontist
40 East Putnam Avenue
Cos Cob, CT 06807
(203) 625-9888

DUSTIN ORTHODONTICS
Dr. Bob Dustin
90 Dearfield Drive
Greenwich, CT 06831
(203) 869-8711

SPECIALISTS

Once you have a pediatrician, he/she will be able to refer you to specialists, should you ever need one. Below is a list of some specialists my friends have referred me to. Please consult with your medical practitioner before acting on health-related issues.

A new trend is **adolescent pediatrics.** Several doctors in Greenwich specialize in adolescent medicine, including:

GLENVILLE MEDICAL ASSOCIATES
7 Riversville Road
Greenwich, CT 06831
(203) 531-1808
www.glenvillemedical.com

DR. MARCIE SCHNEIDER
5 Perryridge Road
Greenwich, CT 06830
(203) 863-4224
This doctor is affiliated with Greenwich Hospital.

Another specialty is the treatment of **eating disorders.**

WILKINS CENTER FOR EATING DISORDERS
7 Riversville Road
Greenwich, CT 06831
(203) 531-1909
www.wilkinscenter.com

ALLERGISTS

FAIRFIELD COUNTY ALLERGY, ASTHMA & IMMUNOLOGY ASSOCIATES, P.C.
148 East Avenue
Suite 3G
Norwalk, CT 06851
(203) 838-4034
www.fcaaia.com
They also have satellite offices in Stamford and Greenwich. The Greenwich office is located at 2 1/2 Dearfield Drive and their phone number is (203) 869-2080.

DERMATOLOGISTS

DR. DEBRA CLAIN
Dermatology Center of Stamford
1290 Summer Street
Stamford, CT 06905
(203) 325-3576

DRS. MICHELE & HENRY GASIOROWSKI
40 West Elm Street
Greenwich, CT 06830
(203) 661-7546

DR. LYNNE HAVEN
49 Lake Avenue
Greenwich, CT 06830
(203) 869-4242

DR. WOODBURY
1200 East Putnam Avenue
Riverside, CT 06878
(203) 637-8114

EAR, NOSE & THROAT

DR. RICHARD J. BRAUER
49 Lake Avenue
Greenwich, CT 06830
(203) 869-0177

DR. STEVEN FELDMAN
4 Dearfield Drive
Greenwich, CT 06831
(203) 629-5500

DR. STEVEN JEFFREY SALZER
Greenwich Ear, Nose & Throat
49 Lake Avenue
Greenwich, CT 06830
(203) 869-2030

EYE DOCTORS

At about age 3 or 4, children should get their eyes checked, especially if one or both parents has poor eyesight.

DR. MICHELE LEVY BASHAN
Optometrist
2 Lafayette Court
Greenwich, CT 06830
(203) 661-4555

STEVEN C. GREENBERG, M.D.
Westchester Medical Group
1 Theall Road
Rye, NY 10580
(914) 253-6502
www.westchestermed.com

GREENWICH OPHTHALMOLOGY
Ophthalmologists
4 Dearfield Road
Greenwich, CT 06830
(203) 869-3082

PHYSICAL THERAPISTS

SAMANTHA BLAZER
Stamford Tully Center
32 Strawberry Hill Court
Stamford, CT 06902
203-276-2660

SPEECH THERAPISTS

GREENWICH HOSPITAL HEARING & SPEECH CENTER
5 Perryridge Rd
Greenwich, CT 06830-4608
(203) 863-3000

JOSEPHINE CHEN CENTER FOR SPEECH AND LANGUAGE PATHOLOGY
JOSEPHINE K. CHEN, M.S., CCC, LLC
Speech Language Pathologists
100 Melrose Avenue, Suite 201
Greenwich, CT 06830
(203) 869-8272
Julie Rosenblum is one of the therapists there who comes highly recommended.

SOIFER CENTER FOR LEARNING AND CHILD DEVELOPMENT
An interdisciplinary private practice of speech and language pathologists
333 Old Tarrytown Road
White Plains, NY 10603
(914) 683-5401

SPORTS MEDICINE

GREENWICH ORTHOPEDIC NEUROSURGERY SPECIALISTS, PC
6 Greenwich Office Park
Valley Drive
Greenwich, CT 06831
(203) 869-1145
www.onsmd.com

A CAUTIONARY NOTE ON CAR SEATS

You tend to do a lot, and I mean a lot, of driving in Greenwich. Therefore, it is vitally important to make sure that your children's car seats are properly installed. Several places in the Greenwich area will install your car seats properly or inspect them for proper installation:

GREENWICH FIRE DEPARTMENT
(203) 622-8087
The Greenwich Fire Department can usually schedule an appointment on the same day. They recommend calling at about 8 a.m. to schedule an appointment.

KID'S HOME FURNISHING
11 Forest Street
Stamford, CT 06901
(203) 327-1333
The Baby Toy and Superstore will install car seats purchased at their store.

AAA OF CONNECTICUT
(203) 765-4222 Ext. 3142
The AAA of Connecticut offers several dates throughout the year when you can get car seat(s) inspected. Call for information.

For additional information on car seat safety, contact **SafeKids** at (203) 667-3246 or the **Greenwich Red Cross** at (203) 869-8444.

EFFECTIVE, OCTOBER 2005, the legislation regarding car seats changed to the following:

- Children over the age of one and over 20 lbs. to children under age seven who weigh less than 60lbs. need to be in car seats.

- Any child under the age of one or weighing less than 20 lbs. needs to be in a rear-facing car seat.

- Children using booster seat need to have a shoulder belt.

For more information, see **www.inventiveparent.com/lawsreg1.htm**.

Chapter 2

CHILD CARE

As it is anywhere, whether you are a working parent or stay-at-home one, child care is a big issue in Greenwich. Before you do anything, first determine how your family's needs can be met. Do you prefer a day care center, an au pair, a nanny? Older or younger nanny? Live-in or live-out? Most often, the form of child care you'll choose will be based on the age of your child, your lifestyle, and your finances. Here I mention only a few of the many options available to you in our town.

DAY CARE

CHILDREN'S DAY SCHOOL
139 East Putnam Avenue
Greenwich, CT 06830
(203) 869-5395
or
8 Riverside Avenue
Riverside, CT 06878
(203) 637-1122
Also known as the **JUNIOR LEAGUE OF GREENWICH CHILD CARE CENTER,** the school is an all-day, year-round day care and preschool for ages 6 weeks to 6 years.

FAMILY CENTERS, INC.
P.O. Box 7550
Greenwich, CT 06836
(203) 869-4848
Family Centers is a preschool learning program for children ages 8 weeks and up. Child care is available from 7:30 a.m. to 6:00 p.m.

Both the **YMCA** and the **YWCA** offer full- and half-day childcare programs. In addition, both have babysitting services available if you want to use the gym or other facilities on the premises.

GREENWICH FAMILY Y CHILD CARE

2 St. Roch Avenue
Greenwich, CT 06830
(203) 869-3381
www.gwymca.org
The Greenwich Family Y offers full child care for ages 6 weeks to 5 years, year-round. There is also a half-day preschool for ages 3–5 and after-school program for Kindergarten–Fifth Grade.

GREENWICH YWCA

259 East Putnam Avenue
Greenwich, CT 06830
(203) 869-6501
www.ywcagreenwich.org

ST PAUL'S EVANGELICAL LUTHERAN CHURCH

761 King Street (at Comly Avenue)
Rye Brook, NY 10573
(914) 939-3079
The church runs a full-day child care center for children ages 6 weeks to 4 years.

TUTOR TIME

25 Valley Drive
Greenwich, CT 06831
(203) 861-6549
www.tutortime.com
Tutor Time is both a day care center and preschool. They have developed a proprietary curriculum to meet the educational and developmental needs of children ages 6 weeks to 6 years.

LITTLE FRIENDS

25 Valley Drive
Greenwich, CT 06830
(203) 861-6549
Little Friends offers high quality childcare and early learning for children ages 6 weeks to 5 years, from 6:30 a.m. – 6:30 p.m., all year round.

AU PAIRS

An au pair is a young woman, 18–26, who comes from abroad to live with you for a year and help you with your children and various domestic chores. In exchange, the au pair develops her English-language skills and learns about American culture as she becomes part of your family. The cost of an au pair is about $250 per week, although the bulk of that payment goes to the au pair agency.

AU PAIR IN AMERICA

Au Pair in America is designated by the Department of State to place qualified international visitors with American host families. They offer a standard program and the Au Pair Extraordinaire program, which offers au pairs who have a formal academic child care degree or two years' full-time experience.

For further information and an application, call (800) 928-7247 or visit the website, www.aupairinamerica.com

AU PAIR USA/INTEREXCHANGE

Au Pair USA is similar to Au Pair in America, but does not provide the "Extraordinaire" program. Au Pair USA is the third-largest au pair program in the United States.
For further information and an application, call (800) Au-Pairs or visit www.interexchange.org.

EURAUPAIR

250 North Pacific Coast Highway
Laguna Beach, CA 92651 USA
Fax: (949) 497-6235
www.euraupair.com
The Euraupair agency offers the option of getting a more experienced au pair (called an "au pair par experience").

AU PAIR CARE

(800) 4.AU.PAIR
www.aupaircare.com

CULTURAL CARE AU PAIR

One Education Street
Cambridge, MA 02141
(800) 333-6056
www.culturalcare.com

NANNIES

Another option, if you're not comfortable with someone who is not fluent in English, is to find a nanny through an agency in America. Usually, these nannies are young women taking a break from college or in that "gap year" after college. This option tends to be more expensive than an au pair. Family friends of ours hired a nanny through Oregon Nannies—she turned out to be an enthusiastic and energetic young woman who was great with children.

Unless the nanny you are planning to hire comes from a well-known source, you might want to check his or her background. There is a website called www.peoplefinder.com where you can access utility records, court records, county records, change of address records, property and business records and a variety of other public records to give you information on a person.

NANNYCARE CONNECTIONS LLC

Premier Nanny Agency
Kimberly Tellus (NY)
(646) 415-8833
kimberly@nannycareconnections.com
www.nannycareconnections.com
Highly qualified, CPR certified nannies from the midwest.

OREGON NANNIES INC.

2170 Bedford Way
Eugene, Oregon 97401
(541) 343-3755
Fax: 541-345-9412
Email: onannies@oregonnannies.com
www.oregonnannies.com

NANNIES OF NEBRASKA

PO Box 2202
Norfolk, NE 68702
(402) 379-2444 or (800) 730-2444
Fax: (402) 379-1898
mail@nanniesofnebraska.com
www.nanniesofnebraska.com

4NANNIES

www.4nannies.com
This company helps families locate nannies, long-term babysitters, and household staff.

There is also a nanny agency right here in Greenwich:

REGAL DOMESTICS
268 Mason Street
Greenwich, CT 06830
(203) 869-0044

And if you're seriously looking into getting a nanny, you might need the services of an accountant who knows the rules when it comes to paying your nanny and making sure that you are complying with IRS regulations. These services provide payroll and tax compliance services, from assistance in obtaining federal identification numbers and Social Security numbers to quarterly and annual filings.

NANNYTAX
52 East 42nd Street
Suite 601
New York, NY 10017
(212) 867-1776
www.nannytax.com

BABYSITTERS

You don't always have to rely on your relatives or the neighbors' kids in those unexpected situations when you suddenly need a sitter. Greenwich has those covered.

THE SITTING SERVICE
Besides babysitting, this service offers pet-, house- and a variety of other sitting services in return for an annual membership fee. I am not sure whether they guarantee that the same person will come to take care of your child/children, but they are a proven, reliable last-minute resource. Their sitters are available for day, evening, weekend and overnight stays.

THE SITTING SERVICE OF CONNECTICUT, LLC
1031 Post Road
Darien, CT 06820
(203) 655-9783
www.thesittingservice.com

GREENWICH HIGH SCHOOL has established a referral program that anyone can call to get a babysitter. The program is based at Greenwich High School during the school year and at **COMMUNITY ANSWERS** at Greenwich Public Library during the summer.

GREENWICH HIGH SCHOOL STUDENT EMPLOYMENT SERVICE
(203) 625-8008
Fax: (203) 861-6893
E-mail: postings@ghs-ses.org
www.ghs-ses.org

High school students will do everything from yardwork, sales, tutoring, computer or office work or babysitting. The Service is open Monday through Friday from 11:30am-2:00pm.

Chapter 3

EDUCATION

Greenwich has an abundance of excellent public and private schools. The decision of where to send your child generally comes down to the environment in which you think your child will thrive, academically and socially.

PRESCHOOLS

There are several factors to consider when looking at preschools:

Philosophy: What is the school's philosophy (i.e., Montessori, Whole Child, Waldorf)? How strongly does it adhere to its philosophy?

Teacher Background: Look at the education and training of the teachers. What are their qualifications? Could they identify a learning or other disability and/or care for a child with a learning or other disability?

Facilities: Check out: the playground, indoor play spaces, access to toys and other materials.

Proximity: You'll probably want to avoid driving more than 20 minutes when your kids are in preschool and are only in class for 2 1/2 to 3 hours a day.

To apply for preschool, make an appointment to visit the school you are interested in, attend the open house, and fill out an application form. You should contact the preschool you are interested in during the fall (generally right after Labor Day) before your child will start school because a lot of acceptances are on a first-come, first-served basis.

BANKSVILLE NURSERY SCHOOL
12 Banksville Road
Greenwich, CT 06831
(203) 661-9715

BRIDGES NURSERY SCHOOL
Greenwich Civic Center
Harding Road
Old Greenwich, CT 06870
(203) 637-0204

BRUNSWICK PRESCHOOL
(boys)
100 Maher Avenue
Greenwich, CT 06830
(203) 625-5800
www.brunswickschool.org

CHRIST CHURCH NURSERY SCHOOL
254 East Putnam Avenue
Greenwich, CT 06830
(203) 869-5334
www.christchurchgreenwich.com

CHILDREN'S DAY SCHOOL
8 Riverside Avenue
Riverside, CT 06878
139 E. Putnam Avenue
Greenwich, CT 06830
(203) 869-5395

THE CHILDREN'S SCHOOL
12 Gary Road
Stamford, CT 06903
(203) 329-8815
www.childrensschool.org

CONVENT OF THE SACRED HEART EARLY LEARNING CENTER
1177 King Street
Greenwich, CT 06831
(203) 531-6500
www.cshgreenwich.org

FAMILY CENTERS PRESCHOOL LEARNING PROGRAMS
(Warburg Infant and Toddler Center)
P.O. Box 7550
Greenwich, CT 06836
(203) 869-4848

FIRST CHURCH PRESCHOOL
108 Sound Beach Avenue
Old Greenwich, CT 06870
(203) 637-5430
www.firstchurchpreschool.org

FIRST PRESBYTERIAN CHURCH NURSERY SCHOOL
37 Lafayette Place
Greenwich, CT 06830
(203) 869-7782
www.fpcg.org

GREENWICH ACADEMY
(girls)
200 North Maple Avenue
Greenwich, CT 06830
(203) 625-8900
www.greenwichacademy.org

GREENWICH FAMILY YMCA SCHOOL
2 Saint Roch Avenue
Greenwich, CT 06830
(203) 869-3380
www.gwymca.org

GREENWICH COUNTRY DAY SCHOOL
P.O. Box 623
Old Church Road
Greenwich, CT 06836-0623
(203) 863-5600
www.gcds.net

GREENWICH PUBLIC SCHOOLS PRESCHOOL
290 Greenwich Avenue
Greenwich, CT 06830
(203) 625-7400
www.greenwichschools.org

THE PRESCHOOL AT SAINT AGNES
247 Stanwich Road
Greenwich, CT 06830
(203) 869-8388

NORTH GREENWICH NURSERY SCHOOL
606 Riversville Road
Greenwich, CT 06831
(203) 869-7945.
www.northgreenwichnurseryschool.com

PUTNAM INDIAN FIELD SCHOOL
101 Indian Field Road
Greenwich, CT 06830
(203) 661-4629
www.pifs.net

ROUND HILL NURSERY SCHOOL
466 Round hill Road
Greenwich, CT 06830
(203) 869-4910
www.roundhillnurseryschool.com

SAINT PAUL CHRISTIAN NURSERY SCHOOL
286 Delavan Avenue
Greenwich, CT 06831
(203) 531-5905

SAINT PAUL'S DAY SCHOOL
200 Riverside Avenue
Riverside, CT 06878
(203) 637-3503

SAINT XAVIER'S CHURCH NURSERY SCHOOL
350 Sound Beach Avenue
Old Greenwich, CT 06870
(203) 698-1303

SELMA MAISEL NURSERY SCHOOL
AT TEMPLE SHOLOM
300 East Putnam Avenue
Greenwich, CT 06830
(203) 622-8121

TINY TOTS SCHOOL
97 Riverside Avenue
Riverside, CT 06878
(203) 637-1398

WHITBY SCHOOL
969 Lake Avenue
Greenwich, CT 06830
(203) 869-8464.
www.whitbyschool.org

WORLDWIDE CHILDREN'S CORNER –
BILINGUAL ENGLISH-JAPANESE SCHOOL
(Greenwich Kokusaigakuen)
521 E. Putnam Avenue
Cos Cob, CT 06830
(203) 629-5567.

YWCA TINKER TOTS
259 East Putnam Avenue
Greenwich
(203) 869-6501 ext.221.
www.ywcagreenwich.org

PUBLIC SCHOOLS

The Greenwich public school system is an excellent one and I strongly urge you to look at your local public school prior to applying to a private school.

For information on **GREENWICH PUBLIC SCHOOLS**, check out the Department of Education's website at www.greenwichschools.org. There are 11 elementary schools, 3 middle schools and 1 high school in the public school system:

COS COB ELEMENTARY SCHOOL
300 East Putnam Avenue
Cos Cob, CT 06807
(203) 869-4670

GLENVILLE ELEMENTARY SCHOOL
33 Riversville Road
Greenwich, CT 06831
(203) 531-9287

**THE RENAISSANCE SCHOOL AT
HAMILTON AVENUE**
Western Jr. Highway
Greenwich, CT 06830
(203) 869-1685

THE INTERNATIONAL SCHOOL AT DUNDEE
55 Florence Road
Riverside, CT 06878
(203) 637-3800

JULIAN CURTISS ELEMENTARY SCHOOL
180 East Elm Street
Greenwich, CT 06830
(203) 869-1896

NEW LEBANON ELEMENTARY SCHOOL
25 Mead Avenue
Greenwich, CT 06830
(203) 531-9139

NORTH MIANUS ELEMENTARY SCHOOL
309 Palmer Hill Road
Riverside, CT 06878
(203) 637-9730

NORTH STREET ELEMENTARY SCHOOL
381 North Street
Greenwich, CT 06830
(203) 869-6756

OLD GREENWICH ELEMENTARY SCHOOL
285 Sound Beach Avenue
Old Greenwich, CT 06870
(203) 637-0150

PARKWAY ELEMENTARY SCHOOL
141 Lower Cross Road
Greenwich, CT 06831
(203)869-7466

RIVERSIDE ELEMENTARY SCHOOL
90 Hendrie Avenue
Riverside, CT 06878
(203) 637-1440

CENTRAL MIDDLE SCHOOL
9 Indian Rock Lane
Greenwich, CT 06830
(203) 661-8500

EASTERN MIDDLE SCHOOL
51 Hendrie Avenue
Riverside, CT 06878
(203) 637-1744

WESTERN MIDDLE SCHOOL
Western Jr. Highway
Greenwich, CT 06830
(203) 531-5700

GREENWICH HIGH SCHOOL
10 Hillside Road
Greenwich, CT 06830
(203) 625-8000

PRIVATE SCHOOLS

All schools are coed unless otherwise specified.

BRUNSWICK SCHOOL FOR BOYS
(boys, pre-K–high school)
100 Maher Avenue
Greenwich, CT 06830
(203) 625-5800
www.brunswickschool.org

CONVENT OF THE SACRED HEART
(girls, pre-K-grade 12)
1177 King Street
Greenwich, CT 06831
(203) 531-6500
www.cshgreenwich.com

EAGLE HILL SCHOOL
(ages 6–16, Special Education)
45 Glenville Road
Greenwich, CT 06831
(203) 622-9240
www.eaglehillschool.org

FAIRFIELD COUNTRY DAY SCHOOL
(K–grade 9)
A School for Boys
2970 Bronson Road
Fairfield, CT 06824
www.fairfieldcountryday.org

GREENWICH ACADEMY
(girls, pre-K–high school)
200 North Maple Avenue
Greenwich, CT 06830
(203) 625-8900
www.greenwichacademy.org

GREENWICH CATHOLIC SCHOOL
(pre-K–grade 8)
471 North Street
Greenwich, CT 06830
(203) 869-4000

GREENWICH COUNTRY DAY SCHOOL
(nursery–grade 9)
P.O. Box 623
Old Church Road
Greenwich CT 06830
(203) 863-5600
www.gcds.net

KING & LOW-HEYWOOD THOMAS SCHOOL
(K-grade 12)
1450 Newfield Avenue
Stamford, CT 06905

(203) 322-3496
www.klht.org

NEW CANAAN COUNTRY SCHOOL
(beginners–grade 9)
545 Ponus Ridge
P.O. Box 997
New Canaan, CT 06840
203.972.0771
www.countryschool.net

RYE COUNTRY DAY SCHOOL
(K–grade12)
Cedar Street
Rye, NY 10580
(914) 967-1417
www.rcds.rye.ny.us

THE MEAD SCHOOL
(nursery–grade 8)
1095 Riverbank Road
Stamford, CT 06903
(203) 595-9500
www.meadschool.org

THE PEAR TREE POINT SCHOOL
(K–grade 5)
90 Pear Tree Point Road
Darien, CT 06820
(203) 655-0030
www.ptpschool.org

THE STANWICH SCHOOL
(pre-K–grade 9)
257 Stanwich Road
Greenwich, CT 06830
(203) 542-0000
www.stanwichschool.org

THE WHITBY SCHOOL
(nursery–grade 8, Montessori System)
969 Lake Avenue
Greenwich, CT 06831
(203) 869-8464
www.whitbyschool.org

TUTORING

It may happen that your child needs some extra help in a certain subject. Or, sometimes, you just need to have someone help your child with his or her homework. Generally, schools have a list of tutors that kids have used and have been recommended, or you can call the Department of Education for referrals at (203) 625-7400. There are also a few larger organizations, listed below. The selection process comes down to where you and your child are most comfortable, both in terms of educators and facilities.

BRIGHT IDEAS TUTORING, LLC
203.966.5897
brightideastutor@aol.com
49 Locust Avenue, Suite 104
New Canaan, CT 06840

DAIC
Developmental Assessment & Intervention Center, LLC
Risa Tabacoff, PhD, MPS, MS,
Director of Services
83 Adams Street
Bedford Hills, New York 10507
(914) 666-7687
www.daic.org
Psychological and educational testing plus solutions for all children.

EVA CLEMENTS, M.A.
Cognitive/Learning Coach
(203) 852-0567
evclements2@yahoo.com
PSAT/SAT prep, Essays, Reading skills, Study skills, IEP/504 Plan Assistance.

GREENWICH ACADEMIC COACHING
(Academic Coaching & Tutoring for grades 5–12)
52 Ute Place #1
Greenwich, CT 06830
203.912.9816
info@GreenwichAcademic.com
Greenwich Academic Coaching specializes in the student that is struggling or underachieving. Academic Coaching focuses on time management, prioritization, homework planning, study habits, goal-setting (academically & personally), motivation, stress reduction, essay writing, subject-specific tutoring.

GREENWICH EDUCATION AND PREP
c/o Educational Services
@ The Water Club
49 River Road
Cos Cob, CT 06807
(203) 661-1609
www.greenwichedprep.com
I have had personal experience with Greenwich Education and Prep and I am very impressed by the quality of the staff and the teaching methods.

HUNTINGTON LEARNING CENTER
1835 Post Road East
Westport, CT
(203) 254-3061
(203) 226-4900
1-800-CAN-LEARN
Private Tutoring for SAT/PSAT, ACT prep, diagnostic testing.

KAPLAN TEST PREP AND ADMISSIONS
1.800.KAP.TEST

LINDAMOOD-BELL LEARNING CENTER
1574 Post Road
Darien, CT 06820
(203) 656-0771

MATHTRENDS/STAMFORD KUMON
MATH AND READING CENTER
111 High Ridge Rd
Stamford, CT 06905
(203) 348-8401

RAGING KNOWLEDGE
Passion for Teaching, Learning and
Community
Ela Mata, President
180 Post Road East
Westport, CT ????
203.226.6981
www.ragingknowledge.com
Skill-Based Tutoring, Subject-Based
Tutoring, Standardized Test
Preparation, Special Services.
Raging Knowledge is a Westport-based
learning center staffed by full-time
education professionals. They are
dedicated to providing the highest
quality educational care for the whole
child. They have been serving Fairfield
County for seven years.

SOIFER CENTER FOR LEARNING
AND CHILD DEVELOPMENT
333 Old Tarrytown Road
White Plains, NY 10603
(914) 683-5401

SYLVAN LEARNING CENTER
(800)611-2715
www.tutoring.sylvanlearning.com

RELIGIOUS EDUCATION

All faiths are represented in
Greenwich, and all offer religious
instruction to children.

Assembly of God:

HARVEST TIME ASSEMBLY OF GOD
1338 King Street
Greenwich, CT 06831
(203) 531-7778

Catholic:

SAINT CATHERINE OF SIENA
4 Riverside Avenue
Riverside, CT 06878
(203) 637-3661

SAINT MARY'S CHURCH
178 Greenwich Avenue
Greenwich, CT 06830
(203) 869-9393

SAINT MICHAEL'S CHURCH
469 North Street
Greenwict, CT 06830
(203) 869-5421

Congregational:

FIRST CONGREGATIONAL CHURCH
108 Sound Beach Avenue
Old Greenwich, CT 06870
(203) 637-1791
www.fccog.org

NORTH GREENWICH CONGREGATIONAL
CHURCH
606 Riversville Road
Greenwich, CT 06831
(203) 869-7763

SECOND CONGREGATIONAL CHURCH
139 East Putnam Avenue
Greenwich, CT 06830
(203) 869-9311
www.2cc.org

STANWICH CONGREGATIONAL CHURCH
202 Taconic Road
Greenwich, CT 06831
(203) 661-4420
www.stanwichchurch.org

Episcopal:

CHRIST CHURCH
254 East Putnam Avenue
Greenwich CT 06830
(203) 869-6600
www.christchurchgreenwich.com

ST. BARNABAS EPISCOPAL CHURCH
954 Lake Avenue
Greenwich, CT 06831
(203) 661-5526
www.stbarnabasgreenwich.org

SAINT PAUL'S EPISCOPAL CHURCH
200 Riverside Avenue
Riverside, Connecticut 06878
(203) 637-2447
www.stpaulsriverside.org

SAINT SAVIOUR'S EPISCOPAL CHURCH
350 Sound Beach Avenue
Old Greenwich, CT 06870
(203) 637-2262
www.saintsaviours.org

Jewish:

CHABAD LUBAVITCH OF GREENWICH
75 Mason Street
Greenwich, CT 06830
(203) 629-9059
www.chabadgreenwich.org

CONGREGATION SHIR AMI
137 Cat Rock Road
Cos Cob, CT 06807
(203) 921-1001

GREENWICH REFORM SYNAGOGUE
257 Stanwich Road
Greenwich, CT 06830
(203) 629-0018

TEMPLE SHOLOM
300 East Putnam Avenue
Greenwich, CT 06830
(203) 869-7191
www.templesholom.com

Lutheran:

FIRST LUTHERAN CHURCH
38 Field Point Road
Greenwich, CT 06830
(203) 869-0032

JAPANESE GOSPEL CHURCH OF GREENWICH
286 Delavan Avenue
Byram, CT 06830
(203) 531-6450
Methodist:

DIAMOND HILL UNITED METHODIST CHURCH
521 East Putnam Avenue
Greenwich, CT 06830
(203) 869-2395

FIRST UNITED METHODIST CHURCH
59 East Putnam Avenue
Greenwich, CT 06830
(203) 629-9584
www.fumcgreenwichcjb.net

Non-Denominational and Community:

DINGLETOWN COMMUNITY CHURCH
Corner of Stanwich Road and
Barnstable Lane
Greenwich, CT 06830
(203) 629-5923

FIRST CHURCH OF ROUND HILL
464 Round Hill Road
Greenwich, CT 06831
(203) 629-3876

ROUND HILL COMMUNITY CHURCH
395 Round Hill Road
Greenwich, CT 06831
(203) 869-1091
www.roundhillcommunitychurch.org

Presbyterian:

FIRST PRESBYTERIAN CHURCH
One West Putnam Avenue
Greenwich CT 06830
(203) 869-8636
www.fpocg.org

GRACE CHURCH OF GREENWICH,
PRESBYTERIAN CHURCH IN AMERICA
THE WOMAN'S CLUB OF GREENWICH
89 Maple Avenue
Greenwich, CT 06830
(203) 861-7555
www.gracechurchgreenwich.com
THE PRESBYTERIAN CHURCH OF
OLD GREENWICH
38 West End Avenue
Old Greenwich, CT 06870
(203) 637-3669
www.pcogonline.org

EDUCATIONAL ORGANIZATIONS

AMERICAN INSTITUTE FOR FOREIGN STUDY
102 Greenwich Avenue
Greenwich, CT 06830
(203) 869-9090
For international students studying
in Japan.

GREENWICH ALLIANCE FOR EDUCATION
P.O. Box 473
Old Greenwich, CT 06870
(203) 698-7730
www.greenwichalliance.org
The Greenwich Alliance for Education
mobilizes community resources to
provide opportunities and services
that foster educational success for
all Greenwich public school students.

PARENTS TOGETHER
P.O. Box 4843
Greenwich, CT 06831-0417
fax: 698-3376
e-mail: togetherparent@aol.com
TogetherParent@aol.com
Providing Communication, Education,
Support and Parenting Resources to
Greenwich Parents.
Parents Together is an independent,
nonprofit organization in Greenwich,
Connecticut founded in 1979 with the
guidance from the Greenwich Council
on Youth and Drugs, the Junior
League of Greenwich, Greenwich
Public School administrators and the
PTA Council. Parents Together offers
ongoing opportunities for parents to
communicate, share, support and
learn together. They have a very
helpful newsletter and interesting
events with prominent speakers.

NOTES

Chapter 4

ACTIVITIES

As far as general kids' activities are concerned, I am of the opinion that kids should have time to be kids and play on their own and shouldn't be in too many activities. When I was young and we had just moved to the United States from France, my mother was so thrilled by all the activities she could sign me up for – which she had never had an opportunity to do – she decided to sign me up for almost everything! Given the bounty of offerings, it is easy to get tempted to sign them up for many activities but it is also important for children to have time to unwind from school and/or play with their siblings.

A couple of general information centers can tell you all about activities and events going on in Greenwich:

COMMUNITY ANSWERS provides every kind of information about the Greenwich community.
(203) 622-7979
www.communityanswers.org

KIDSEVENTS.COM is a comprehensive online resource for information about events and classes. Kids' Events also publishes an annual Birthday Guide and a Summer Camp Guide.
www.kidsevents.com

Free publications such as *Westchester Family* and *Fairfield County Kids*, available at super-markets, list events and other useful information for children and families. *ACORN*, which comes out twice a year in the local newspaper, lists activities and events for children and families.

ACTIVITY CENTERS

Both of the Ys in Greenwich offer a multitude of activities for children, from 6 months to age 12. They are often a good "first stop," as they not only have a wide selection of programs for young children but tend to be a bit more reasonably priced than other programs in town.

GREENWICH YWCA
259 East Putnam Avenue
Greenwich, CT 06830
(203) 869-6501
www.ywcagreenwich.org

GREENWICH YMCA
50 East Putnam Avenue
Greenwich, CT 06830
(203) 869-1630
www.gwymca.org

One of the many programs the Greenwich YMCA offers is **Adventure Guides**. This is a father-child program for grades K-3. Dads and their sons or daughters join one of the Greenwich "Tribes" and enjoy many fun outdoor, social and service activities. Contact Deb Marchese at the Greenwich Family Y for more information: (203) 869-1630.

The **OLD GREENWICH–RIVERSIDE COMMUNITY CENTER**, also known as **THE OGRCC**, offers a variety of recreational, athletic, educational and social programs for children. For information on programs, contact:

OLD GREENWICH-RIVERSIDE COMMUNITY CENTER (OGRCC)
90 Harding Road
Old Greenwich, CT 06870
(203) 637-3659
www.ogrcc.com

GREENWICH BOYS AND GIRLS CLUB
4 Horseneck Lane
Greenwich, CT 06830
(203) 869-3224
www.bgcg.org

The **GREENWICH DEPARTMENT OF PARKS AND RECREATION** does not stint on children's sports and other fun events. Get in touch and find out what's up this season:

GREENWICH DEPARTMENT OF PARKS AND RECREATION
101 Field Point Road
P.O. Box 2540
Greenwich, CT 06836
(203) 622-7814
(203) 622-7830
www.greenwichct.org

KIDS U
633 Hope Street
Stamford, CT 06907
(203) 358-9500
www.kids-u.com
Kids U offers classes in many disciplines including gymnastics, music, martial arts, dance, theater, cooking, science, and sports and games for children ages 1-9. They also have a location in Westport.

NORWALK COMMUNITY COLLEGE offers a program called **COLLEGE FOR KIDS** which runs during the months of March and April, and then in summer. They offer a wide variety of classes for children who are in grades K-8, such

as cooking, fashion design, watercolor painting, cartooning and many more.
(203) 857-3337
www.nctc.commnet.edu

For art, music, performance and language classes, try the following:

THE GREENWICH ARTS COUNCIL
299 Greenwich Avenue
Greenwich, CT 06830
(203) 622-3998
www.greenwicharts.org
The Greenwich Arts Council offers language, dance, art and music classes for children and adults.

THE RYE ARTS CENTER
51 Milton Road
Rye, NY 10580
(914) 967-0700
www.ryeartscenter.org
The Rye Arts Center has a wide and in-depth selection of art, music and performing arts classes for children and adults. Their programs and workshops are very good.

For very young children, there is one main general program:

JUST WEE TWO
(ages 16 months - 3 1/2 years)
(800) 404-2204
www.justweetwo.com
Just Wee Two is a preschool-preparation program that has a well-earned fine reputation. They have 90-minute classes in a range of activities: arts & crafts, music, stories, playtime, and creative movement. They also offer "separation programs" for 2- to 3 - year-olds who are learning to have fun without Mommy present.
Just Wee Two has locations in Greenwich and North Stamford.

LIBRARIES

The Greenwich Library is a great resource. In addition to a large children's section, the library offers story time for babies and kids, and reading clubs for older kids. The library has branches in Byram, Cos Cob, and Old Greenwich. Each branch offers innovative and active programs for children.

GREENWICH LIBRARY
101 West Putnam Avenue
Greenwich, CT 06830
(203) 622-7900
www.greenwichlibrary.org

BYRAM-SHUBERT LIBRARY
21 Mead Avenue
Greenwich, CT 06830
(203) 531-0426

COS COB BRANCH LIBRARY
5 Sinawoy Road
Cos Cob, CT 06807
(203) 622-6883

PERROT MEMORIAL LIBRARY
90 Sound Beach Avenue
Old Greenwich, CT 06870
(203) 637-8802
The Perrot Memorial Library has an especially good book club called "The Young Critics Club", in which children read and review new books from the current year, some even before they are sold in stores.

ACTING & DANCE

In Greenwich we're close enough to New York to have several acting programs for budding child stars, or for kids who just want to express themselves.

THE ACTOR'S GARAGE
(866) 627-7211
info@theactorsgarage.com
www.theactorsgarage.com
The Actor's Garage teaches acting to children ages 4 and up, with a focus on commercials and television, with beginners' classes in concentration, relaxation, and improvisation. The goal is to build self-confidence, trust and comfort in group situations.

MMM PRODUCTIONS
64 West Hill Circle
Stamford, CT 06902
(203) 273-7827
www.mmmproductions.biz
MMM Productions, a theatre arts school offers classes in drama, dance, voice and musical theatre for ages 6-17 years old.

AMERICAN BALLET THEATRE AT THE YWCA
259 East Putnam Avenue
Greenwich, CT 06830
(203) 869-6501
www.abt.org
At ABT's Ballet Program for the Young Dancer, held at the YWCA of Greenwich, children will develop imagination, strengthen motor skills, improve self-discipline, and experience firsthand the magic behind American Ballet Theatre. The program combines weekly ballet technique classes, workshop experiences, and performance viewing opportunities—adding up to a wonderful introduction to ballet study. The program is designed for children ages 4 through 12.

ALLEGRA DANCE STUDIO
37 West Putnam Avenue
Greenwich, CT 06830
(203) 629-9162

BALLET DES ENFANTS
A Fairytale Ballet for Little Dancers with Big Imaginations
2000 West Main Street
The ShopRite Plaza
Stamford, CT 06902
(203) 973-0144
and
722 Post Road
Darien, CT
(203) 662-9800
www.balletdesenfants.net
Each fairytale ballet class brings together dance and music with children's literature, costumes and props. 2-8 years.

CHILDREN'S THEATER COMPANY
Be Mused Productions
Kim Breden, CEM
508 Warburton Avenue, Suite #3
Yonkers, NY 10701
(914) 423-2063
www.bemusedproductions.com
The Children's Theater Company is designed to serve families and children in the tri-state area. Be Mused Productions offers musical theatre workshops which are performance oriented However, they do not require any previous experience or skill level. All children learn musical theatre craft and skills such as stage deportment, memorization, projection, and excellent diction. All workshops culminate in a live stage performance complete with costumes, props and scenery.

**CHINESE LANGUAGE SCHOOL
OF CONNECTICUT**
P.O. Box 515
Riverside, CT 06878
(866) 301-4906
www.chineselanguageschool.org
Chinese Folk Dance classes are
taught by a professional dance
instructor from the New York Chinese
Cultural Center (NYCCC). The NYCCC
Dance School is the only full time
professional school of Chinese dance
in the U.S.

CURTAIN CALL PERFORMANCE WORKSHOPS
1349 Newfield Avenue
Stamford, CT 06905
(203) 329-8207 ext: 16
www.curtaincallinc.com
Curtain Call is a non-profit community
theater company based in Stamford,
CT. They provide workshops for
beginners up to seasoned performers
in all areas of the dramatic arts.

DANCE ADVENTURE
230 Mason Street
Greenwich, CT 06830
(203) 625-0930
www.danceadventure.com
Dance Adventure has youth and
movement classes for children 6
months to 12 years. They also
organize birthday parties. My kids
have taken dance classes here and
also have had their birthday
parties here—both were great.

FANCY FEET DANCE STUDIO
40 Gold Street
Greenwich, CT 06830
(203) 532-4521
Fancy Feet Dance Studio is a new
dance studio in Greenwich. They
offer lessons in Ballet, Tap,
Jazz/Hip-Hop, Gymnastics and

Creative Movement for children
and adults.

JOHN ROBERT POWERS
Modeling and Acting Academy
(203) 853-0080

NEW DANCE
9 Rye Ridge Plaza
Rye Brook, NY 10573
(914) 690-9300
www.newdance.net

THE RYE ARTS CENTER
51 Milton Road
Rye, NY 10580
(914) 967-0700
www.ryeartscenter.org
Ballet, voice and drama classes.

ART

ART CLASSES FOR KIDS
Betsy Beach
304 Wilton Road
Westport, CT
(203) 454.9831
betsybeach@optonline.net
www.betsybeach.com

ARTKIDS
Natasha Schlesinger
(646) 201-9168
www.artmuseny.com
ARTKIDS was created by Natasha
Schlesinger. Natasha Schlesinger is
an independent art historian and an
art consultant who has been working
in the art field for the past 12 years,
specializing in the history of decora-
tive arts. ARTKIDS holds weekly
after-school classes that introduce
children to the excitement of visiting
New York City museums, and also

offers specialized tours for specific classes or schools as well as private tours to specially-chosen museums for out-of-town visitors and their children. ARTKIDS offers birthday party packages, too.

COME OUT AND CLAY
59 North Main Street
South Norwalk, CT 06854
(203) 838-3815
Come Out and Clay offers arts & crafts programs and walk-in activities for children.

THE GREENWICH ARTS COUNCIL
299 Greenwich Avenue
Greenwich, CT 06830
(203) 622-3998
www.greenwicharts.org
The Greenwich Arts Council offers an after-school arts program.

THE GREENWICH ART SOCIETY STUDIO SCHOOL
299 Greenwich Avenue
Greenwich, CT 06830
(203) 629-1533
www.greenwichartsociety.com
The Greenwich Art Society has a Studio School that offers painting classes and art workshops for children and adults.

LAKESIDE POTTERY
543 Newfield Avenue
Stamford, CT 06905
(203) 323-2222
www.lakesidepottery.com
Lakeside Pottery is a very good pottery school, gallery and studio, which offers classes for adults and children. One can also come during their open studio hours and select a piece of pottery to work on.

LITTLE REMBRANDT
116 South Ridge Street
Rye Brook, NY 10573
(914) 939-1400
www.littlerembrandt.info/home.html
Little Rembrandt offers several crafts programs for children. In addition, you can just walk in and select a piece of pottery to paint on the spot. My kids really enjoy painting ceramic pieces—plus, they make perfect gifts. Grandma is always so proud!

PAPER SCISSORS ORANGES
551 Post Road
Darien, CT 06820
(203) 656-2706
www.paperscissorsorganges.com

THE RYE ARTS CENTER
51 Milton Road
Rye, NY 10580
(914) 967-0700
www.ryeartscenter.org
Art, photography and clay classes.

SILVERMINE GUILD ARTS CENTER
1037 Silvermine Rd.
New Canaan, CT 06840
(203) 966-9700
www.silvermineart.org
The Silvermine Guild Arts Center is very well-renowned for its art classes and summer art camps.

CHESS

My friend's son – who is an excellent chess player – plays chess with **MASTER SUNIL WEERAMANTRY.** He is the Executive Director of the National Scholastic Chess Foundation (NSCF). NSCF Instructors are available for private lessons.

For further information, call the
NSCF office at (914) 683-5322.

ETIQUETTE

The social graces have not been for-
gotten in Greenwich. Several places
offer ballroom dancing and etiquette
classes for children:

THE BARCLAY CLASSES OF GREENWICH
Round Hill Community House
397 Round Hill Road
Greenwich, CT 06830
(908) 232-8370
Dancing and etiquette classes for
children in grades four through six.

**MAYFAIR BALLROOM DANCING FOR
YOUNG CHILDREN**
Dorina Link
(203) 869-7016
The Mayfair programs, ballroom
dancing and etiquette for children
in grades four through six, are
sponsored by the Brunswick Parents
Association but are open to children
whose parents are not members.

YOUNG ETIQUETTE
591 Riversville Road
Greenwich, CT 06831
(203) 629-6123
The name says it. The focus is on
etiquette for young children.

FOREIGN LANGUAGES

ALLIANCE FRANCAISE OF GREENWICH
At Greenwich Arts Center
299 Greenwich Avenue
Greenwich, CT 06830
(203) 629-2302

www.afgreenwich.org
The Alliance Francaise of Greenwich
offers a variety of immersion, after-
school and bilingual programs for
children and adults.

**CHINESE LANGUAGE SCHOOL OF
FAIRFIELD COUNTY**
Rippowam Middle School
381 High Ridge Road
Stamford, CT 06902
(203) 341-9557
www.chineseschool-ct.org
The Chinese Language School of
Fairfield County offers Chinese
language classes. They also offer
programs on Chinese culture.

ITALIAN FOR TODDLERS
Greenwich Catholic School
471 North Street
Greenwich, CT 06830
(212) 501-8524
www.italianfortoddlers.com
Italian for Toddlers is a language
program for infants, toddlers and
young children.

LINGUAKIDS
P.O. Box 2662
Darien, CT 06820
(203) 655-6461
www.linguakids.com
Linguakids has classes in French
and Spanish for children ages 2
through 8. Multiple locations in
Darien, Westport, Fairfield, Trumbull,
New Canaan, and Ridgefield.

THE LANGUAGE EXCHANGE
Mill Pond Shopping Center
205 East Putnam Avenue #9
Cos Cob, CT 06807
(203) 422-2024
www.foreignlanguageexchange.com
Classes in Spanish, French, German,

Italian, Dutch, Russian, Mandarin-Chinese, Japanese and Danish, and English as a second language classes for both children and adults.

**THE FRENCH AMERICAN SCHOOL
OF NEW YORK**
111 Larchmont Avenue
Larchmont, NY 10538
(914) 834-3002
www.fasny.org

**THE CHINESE LANGUAGE SCHOOL
OF CONNECTICUT**
P.O. Box 515
Riverside, CT 06878
(866) 301-4906
www.chineselanguageschool.org
Mandarin Chinese language and cultural instruction for children ages 2 1/2 & up. Sunday classes are held at Eastern Middle School in Riverside. Private and semi-private language programs on weekdays and weekends are available. (Chinese Martial Arts and Folk Dance classes are also offered on Sundays at Eastern Middle School.)

THE GERMAN SCHOOL
135 School Road
Weston, CT
(203) 222-1228
www.germanschoolct.org
German language and cultural instruction for novice to native speakers, both children and adults.

THE GREENWICH JAPANESE SCHOOL
15 Ridgeway Lane
Greenwich, CT 06831
(203) 629-5922
www.gwjs.org

MUSIC

**ATELIER CONSTANTIN POPESCU AND
THE RIVERSIDE SCHOOL OF MUSIC**
1139 East Putnam Avenue
Greenwich, CT 06878
(203) 637-7421
www.atelierconstantinpopescu.com

CURTIS FORBES
(206) 931-2128
curtis@curtisforbes.com or
c1forbes@aol.com
www.curtisforbes.com
Whether you are interested in learning jazz or blues, rock, funk, or fusion guitar, Curtis' specialized teaching method approaches each style as a language, and focuses on the significant rhythmic and melodic nuance that creates that unique language. A variety of performance techniques are covered in addition to basic, fundamental mechanics.

GREENWICH MUSIC
1200 East Putnam Avenue
Riverside, CT 06878
(800) 630-3615
www.greenwichmusic.com
Instruction in voice and various instruments.

CONNECTICUT SCHOOL OF MUSIC
1242 Post Road East
Westport, CT 06880
(203) 226-0805
info@ctschoolofmusic.com
www.ctmusicschoolofmusic.com
Founded in 2000, the Connecticut School of Music offers instruction in a variety of instruments as well as studies in ear training, music theory and chamber music.

GREENWICH ALLIANCE FOR EDUCATION

P.O. Box 473
Old Greenwich, CT 06870
(203) 698-7730
www.greenwichalliance.org
The Greenwich Alliance for Education mobilizes community resources to provide opportunities and services that foster educational success for all Greenwich public school students. In their TUNING INTO MUSIC program, students in the Greenwich Public School System who have limited resources and who show an aptitude for instrumental music, as identified by their ensemble and general music teachers, will be provided with every-thing necessary (private instruction, instrument, sheet music and trans-portation) to fulfill their potential as music students and to participate in school orchestras and bands through high school.

GREENWICH SUZUKI ACADEMY

254 E. Putnam Avenue
Greenwich, CT 06830
(203) 561-6176
mailing address:
15 E. Putnam Ave #176
Greenwich, CT 06830
www.greenwichsuzukiacademy.org
Offers private and semi-private lessons, group classes, parent training, and chamber music. Instruction on violin, viola, cello for ages 3 and up.

KINDERMUSIK

Sayre Lukason
Old Greenwich Music Studio
23 Clark Street
Old Greenwich, CT 06870
(203) 637-0461
Kindermusik is an interactive class for children and parents that includes singing, movement, and playing simple instruments. For newborns to 3 years.

MARY ANN HALL'S MUSIC FOR CHILDREN

(203) 854-9797 or
(877) YES-MUSIC
www.musicforchildren.net
Based on the belief that every child is born with natural musical intelligence, Mary Ann Hall has created an exciting and multidimensional program that en-ables children to discover, develop and celebrate their own individual talents. Music for children focuses on your child as the primary instrument through which the music flows and grows.

MUSIC TOGETHER

(203) 256-1656
www.musictogether.com
The Music Together approach develops every child's birthright of basic music competence by encouraging the actual experiencing of music rather than the learning of concepts or information about music. Music Together offers music and movement classes for children from newborn through age 5, as well as for their parents, teachers, and other primary caregivers.

I took several Music Together classes with my fourth child and she absolutely adored them! The instructors and music are engaging and fun. However, choosing a music class is a personal choice so I would suggest that you try out a class (most programs will allow you to take the first class free).

MUSIKA

In Westchester
(914) 833-7595
In Fairfield
(203) 625-9452

Created by a group of teachers, Musika offers dynamic music lessons at your home or in their studios for children ages 4 and up.

SYMMETRY SOUND EXPERIENCE is a music performance and recording program developed and run by Joe Fattorini and Vinny Nobile. They also provide music lessons for various instruments. For more information, contact Vinny at (914) 980-3082 or Joe at (347) 432-8669.

THE MUSIC SOURCE
1345 East Putnam Avenue
Greenwich, CT 06870
(203) 698-0444
Instruction in voice and various instruments.

THE RYE ARTS CENTER
51 Milton Road
Rye, NY 10580
(914) 967-0700
www.ryeartscenter.org
This center has a wonderful offering of voice and instrument classes, as well as a Suzuki School.

If your child is learning how to play an instrument, I would recommend renting the instrument for a while to make sure that your child is really committed to playing. There is nothing worse than purchasing the instrument, only to find that after several months your child is no longer interested in learning how to play the violin, guitar or piano!
To purchase or rent a musical instrument, visit these places in Greenwich:

ATELIER CONSTANTIN POPESCU AND THE RIVERSIDE SCHOOL OF MUSIC
1139 East Putnam Avenue
Greenwich, CT 06878
(203) 637-7421
www.atelierconstantinpopescu.com

THE MUSIC SOURCE
1345 East Putnam Avenue
Greenwich, CT 06870
(203) 698-0444

GREENWICH MUSIC
1200 East Putnam Avenue
Riverside, CT 06878
(800) 630-3615
www.greenwichmusic.com

OTHER CLASSES

A center offering computer classes for kids recently opened in Greenwich. They have different types of classes for young children, ages 3-7, and older children, ages 8-15. The Greenwich location is called **CYBER DISCOVERIES 2** and they can be reached at (877) 376-0048 or www.cyberdiscoveries.com.

In addition to its birthday parties, **AUX DELICES** offers **cooking classes** for kids. They have a variety of interesting classes, such as cake decorating or after school snacks. For more information, call (203) 326-4540 ext. 108. Classes are held at a facility in Stamford.

Restaurateur **BANDY ACCIAVATTI** of **KIDS 'R' COOKIN** offers **cooking classes** for kids, as well as **cooking birthday parties.** (914) 937-2012
bandy@kidsrcookin.com

OUTINGS

When I moved to Greenwich, I was surprised and excited to find so many places to visit: museums, aquariums, zoos, all within easy driving distance. Add to these the theaters, amusement parks, and – something you'd never find in New York City! – a farm and petting zoo, which kids go crazy for. Following is your guide to this wealth of interesting and fun outings.

First and foremost, Greenwich has many great parks and playgrounds – we especially like **BRUCE PARK** (opposite the Bruce Museum). A fun thing to do is go there around 3:30-4:00pm when the ice cream truck comes. Bruce Park also has tennis and bocce ball courts.
In Old Greenwich, there is **BINNEY PARK**, which also has a playground, tennis courts, and ball fields.
ROGER SHERMAN BALDWIN PARK is located off of Arch Street, next to the ferry landing for **ISLAND BEACH** and **GREAT CAPTAINS ISLAND**. The Park has a Skatepark for kids ages six and up (with a pass). In summer, the town has outdoor concerts and performances in the park, which are always fun to attend as a group.

TOD'S POINT, as the Greenwich beach is known, is a paradise for all little kids, and big ones too! Little kids can have fun in the shallow wading pools and older kids can swim in the water – there are lifeguards there to watch over the kids. Tod's Point has two snack bars, a picnic area, outdoor showers, a biking or rollerblading path, a rock garden, a clambake area and a marina. In summer, they hold an annual sandcastle contest and kite flying event. If you call the Department of Parks and Recreation, you can also reserve an area for parties.
BYRAM BEACH has a beach and swimming pool, a clambake area, softball fields, tennis courts, a boat dock and playground.

One of our favorite things to do in summer is take the ferry to **ISLAND BEACH**. Island Beach and **GREAT CAPTAINS ISLAND** are two small islands located about 2 miles away from Greenwich Harbor. Island Beach has a snack bar and playground. If you apply early enough, you can get a permit to camp overnight at Island Beach – a great birthday party idea! The ferries run from mid-June through mid-September. On weekends, there is also the **CRUISE TO NOWHERE,** which is a two-hour cruise around the islands.

Your beach card application usually comes in the mail, or you can pick it up at the Greenwich Town Hall. If you would like to bring a guest to the beach, you can purchase a single-visit ticket for $10 or a ten-visit guest pass for $60 at Town Hall (Monday-Friday from 8:30am-3:30pm) or the Eastern Greenwich Civic Center (Daily, 9am-5pm). Tod's Point and Byram Beach are open year-round, but beach passes are required from May to September. When you receive your beach pass, you get information on ferry timings and other summer concerts in town. Contact the Greenwich Department of Parks and Recreation at (203) 622-7814 or check out www.greenwichct.org.

MUSEUMS

AMERICAN MUSEUM OF NATURAL HISTORY
Central Park West at 79th Street
New York, NY 10024
(212) 769-5100
www.amnh.org
Hours: Sunday - Thursday 10 A.M. –
5:45 P.M., Fridays and Saturdays,
10 A.M. – 8:45 P.M.
The American Museum of Natural
History is one of the finest institu-
tions for research and education into
the natural sciences. The museum is
great for kids, with lots of fascinating
permanent exhibits and special programs and workshops. We especially
like the dinosaur exhibit and the
dioramas of the Native Americans.

BARNUM MUSEUM
820 Main Street
Bridgeport, CT 06604
(203) 331-1104
www.barnum-museum.org
The Barnum Museum has a commitment to the preservation and inter-
pretation of nearby Bridgeport's
industrial and social history, with a
special focus on P. T. Barnum, the
creator of the Barnum and Bailey
Circus, who was born here.
Hours: Tuesday – Saturday 10 A.M. –
4:30 P.M., Sunday 12 P.M – 4:30 P.M.

BRUCE MUSEUM
1 Museum Drive
Greenwich, CT 06830
(203) 869-0376
www.brucemuseum.org
The Bruce is a small but wonderful
art and science museum with a very
manageable area geared to younger
kids with dioramas and a touch tank.
For children ages 6 to12, there are

special art programs. Call the
Education Department at
(203) 869-6786 for more information.
Hours: Tuesday–Saturday, 10 A.M. –
5 P.M, Sunday, 1 P.M. – 5 P.M.

DONALD M. KENDALL SCULPTURE GARDENS
Pepsico World Headquarters
700 Andersen Hill Road
Purchase, NY 10577
While not quite a museum, the Donald
M. Kendall Sculpture Gardens at
Pepsico Headquarters in Purchase are
quite amazing. The sculpture collec-
tion was begun in 1965 and now con-
sists of 45 works by major twentieth-
century artists. The sculptures and
gardens exist in harmony on about
168 acres of land. A drive of about
15-20 minutes from Greenwich. We
like to pack a picnic and hang out
at the Gardens!

**HISTORICAL SOCIETY OF THE
TOWN OF GREENWICH**
Bush-Holley Historic Site
39 Strickland Road
Cos Cob, CT 06807
(203) 869-6899
www.hstg.org
The first art colony in Connecticut
was located in Cos Cob. From 1890
to 1920, art students studied with
leading American impressionist
painters at the Holley family's
boardinghouse, which is now a
museum. Besides the
BUSH-HOLLEY MUSEUM, the Historical
Society of Greenwich conducts
one-day family and children's
programs, such as scarecrow-making
workshops, and workshops to make
old-fashioned toys and games.
To register for programs, call
(203) 869-6899. Hours: Wednesday-
Sunday 12 P.M. – 4 P.M.

MANHATTAN CHILDREN'S MUSEUM
212 West 83d Street
New York, NY 10024
(203) 721-1234
www.cmom.org
I think that if you are going to take your child to a children's museum, it should be the Stepping Stones Museum for Children. However, the Manhattan Children's Museum is close to the Museum of Natural History so, if you are feeling particularly energetic, it could be a nice pit-stop.
Hours: Wednesday—Sunday, 10 A.M. – 5 P.M.

MYSTIC SEAPORT - THE MUSEUM OF AMERICA AND THE SEA
75 Greenmanville Avenue
PO Box 6000
Mystic, CT 06355-0990
(860) 572-5315
www.mysticseaport.org
Mystic Seaport Museum is the largest and most comprehensive maritime museum in North America. There are replicas of traditional wooden boats and antique steamboats, a restored village with forty historic buildings, including a schoolhouse, pharmacy, and bank. The Seaport Museum is open from April to October, 10 A.M. – 4 P.M.; and from November to March, 9 A.M. – 5 P.M.

STEPPING STONES MUSEUM FOR CHILDREN
Mathews Park
303 West Avenue
Norwalk, CT 06850
(203) 899-0606
www.steppingstonesmuseum.org
My family loves this museum, especially the water area, and the mock helicopter and submarine. Children 1–7 enjoy the variety of exhibits, as well as special times for crafts and books.
Hours: Tuesday 12 P.M. – 5 P.M., Wednesday – Sunday 10 A.M. – 5 P.M.

NATURE CENTERS

AUDUBON SOCIETY OF GREENWICH
613 Riversville Road
Greenwich, CT 06831
(203) 869-5272
www.greenwich.center.audubon.org
Situated on a 400-acre sanctuary, the Audubon Society of Greenwich has many trails and nature exhibits, as well as nature programs for children. The Center can also be booked for birthday parties for children.
Hours: Monday-Sunday 9 A.M. – 5 P.M.

NEW CANAAN NATURE CENTER
144 Oenoke Ridge
New Canaan, CT 06840
(203) 966-9577
www.newcanaannature.org
This beautiful environmental education center and sanctuary is dedicated to helping people of all ages understand and care for the world of nature. In addition to varied educational programs, the Center has a preschool focusing on environmental education. The Center can also be booked for birthday parties for children ages 3–12.

NEW YORK BOTANICAL GARDENS
Bronx River Parkway at Fordham Road
Bronx, NY 10458
(718) 817-8700
www.nybg.org
We recently went to the New York Botanical Gardens in the Bronx and absolutely loved it! The gardens are beautiful, the Children's Garden is a lot of fun and the whole atmosphere

is great. The best part is that the Gardens are only about 20 minutes away from Greenwich.

SOUNDWATERS CENTER
1281 Cove Road
Stamford, CT 06902
(203) 323-1978
www.soundwaters.org
From here you can take a sail with SoundWaters Ecology Sails. On their impressive 80-foot schooner replica, you will help raise the sails and get to examine sea creatures from four different stations in the Long Island Sound.

STAMFORD MUSEUM & NATURE CENTER
39 Scotfieldtown Road
Stamford, CT 06903
(203) 322-1646
www.stamfordmuseum.org
This is an actual working farm that children can explore and learn about farm life and farm animals. There is also a small museum— art and nature programs for children are offered here, too— and a playground. The Center can also be booked for birthday parties for children. Hours: Open year-round, except for major holidays, Monday–Saturday 9 A.M. – 5 P.M., Sunday, 1 P.M. – 5 P.M.

ZOOS

BEARDSLEY ZOO
1875 Noble Avenue
Bridgeport, CT 06610
(203) 394-6565
www.beardsleyzoo.org
The Beardsley Zoo is Connecticut's only accredited zoo. However, I add the caveat that the cages at the Beardsley Zoo seem small for the animals. Hours: Open year-round from 9 A.M. – 4 P.M.

BRONX ZOO
2300 Southern Boulevard
Bronx, NY 10460
(718) 220-5100
www.bronxzoo.com
In spring and summer, this is our favorite place to go (and it's closer to Greenwich than the Beardsley Zoo!). The Bronx Zoo is magnificent—a wide range of animals, reptiles, birds, and countless exhibits — you can do as much or as little as you wish. Besides all the animals to see, there are exciting rides for the kids, such as the Bengali Monorail, which takes you through an exhibit of Asian animals by train. Hours: Monday – Sunday, 10 A.M. – 5 P.M.

AQUARIUMS

Although the Brooklyn and Mystic aquariums are rather far from Greenwich, and it's advisable to plan an entire day for an excursion to either, the benefit of both is that they offer a number of other attractions nearby. The Mystic Aquarium is close to Mystic Seaport and the Brooklyn Aquarium is located in Coney Island with its colorful amusement park—both interesting and historic places. I highly recommend both of these aquariums; they have a wide variety of specimens, including dolphins, whales, and sharks. Moreover, both have a user-friendly, well-designed layout—I especially like that I can view the fish from above and below the water.

BROOKLYN AQUARIUM
610 Surf Avenue
Brooklyn, NY 11224
(718) 265-3472
www.nyaquarium.com

**MYSTIC AQUARIUM & INSTITUTE
FOR EXPLORATION**
55 Coogan Boulevard
Mystic, CT 06355
(860) 572-5955
www.mysticaquarium.org
Combined with the Seaport Museum, it
makes for a terrific day-trip, definitely
worth the 2-hour drive from Greenwich. Mystic Aquarium is open daily,
year-round, except Christmas Day.

NORWALK AQUARIUM
10 North Water Street
Norwalk, CT 06854
(203) 852-0700
www.maritimeaquarium.org
Hours: The Aquarium is open daily,
year-round. From September to June,
10 A.M. – 5 P.M., July to Labor Day,
10 A.M. – 6 P.M.
Right here in Fairfield County, we
have a smaller but excellent aquarium, which is especially manageable
for younger children. The Norwalk
Aquarium has many exhibits on fish
from the area, with a focus on smaller
fish. A plus is their IMAX movie theater, which is simply quite amazing.

FARMS & PETTING ZOOS

EDEN FARMS
947 Stillwater Rd.
Stamford, CT 06902
(203) 325-3445
www.edenfarmsllc.com
Eden Farms has special celebrations

for seasonal events to please the
entire family: Easter bunnies and egg
hunts, Halloween hayrides, pony rides,
pumpkin patch, a haunted house and
a hay bale maze. Santa and his
farm animals visit every weekend
in December.

**HECKSCHER FARM AT THE STAMFORD
MUSEUM & NATURE CENTER**
39 Scotfieldtown Road
Stamford, CT 06903
(203) 322-1646
www.stamfordmuseum.org
This small working farm has pigs,
sheep, and some very large cows! It is
a nice short tour for very young kids.

SILVERMAN'S FARM
451 Sport Hill Road
Easton, CT
(203) 261-3306
www.silvermansfarm.com
We found Silverman's Farm soon after
we moved to Greenwich, and our kids
just loved seeing what a farm is like
and seeing animals up close at the
small petting zoo. In summer, Silverman's offers peach-picking and, in the
fall, apple-picking, tractor rides, and
a pumpkin patch. Their pies and other
baked goods are delicious.

**STONE BARNS CENTER FOR FOOD
AND AGRICULTURE**
630 Bedford Road
Pocantico Hills, NY 10591
(914) 366-6200
www.stonebarnscenter.org
Stone Barns Center for Food and
Agriculture is a beautiful non-profit
farm, educational center and restaurant in Westchester County. Their
mission is to demonstrate, teach and
promote sustainable, community-
based food production. This is a

lovely place to come with or without children. They offer interesting programs for adults and children. The best part is the restaurant, *Blue Hill*, and the café, which serve delicious foods with ingredients fresh from the farm.

OUTDOOR ADVENTURES

AUDUBON SOCIETY OF GREENWICH
613 Riversville Road
Greenwich, CT 06831
(203) 869-5272
www.greenwich.center.audubon.org
The Audubon Center has open trails for guided or unguided walks, including the **FAIRCHILD FLOWER GARDENS** located on North Porchuck Road.

MIANUS RIVER PARK
Cognewaugh Road
Greenwich, CT
(203) 622-0522
This park is an ideal spot for hiking, jogging, or horseback riding. There are a network of trails varying in difficulty which you can hike on with or without children and pets. We really like to hike there with our kids and dogs.

Other good places to get out in the woods to hike and climb are:
MONTGOMERY PINETUM and
BABCOCK PRESERVE, off of
North Street.
Maps are available at the
GARDEN EDUCATION CENTER
in Cos Cob:
130 Bible Street
Cos Cob, CT
(203) 869-9242

PLAY SPACES

ADVENTURE KIDS
Old Track Road
Greenwich, CT
(203) 861-2227
I personally am not fond of indoor play spaces—the level of hygiene makes me nervous! But if you can get there early, Adventure Kids is a good place to take your kids on a rainy day. Pinball machines and other games, as well as a large activity space give kids plenty to do.

FUN FOR KIDS & GROWNUPS TOO
370 West Main Street
Stamford, CT 06902
(203) 326-5656
www.fun4kidsarcade.com
Fun for Kids & Grownups Too opened not too long ago in Stamford. They have a soft play area, an arcade, laser tag, and many other activities for, well, kids and grown-ups.

GREAT PLAY
A unique new gym for Kids
2000 W. Main St.
Stamford, CT 06902
(203) 978-1333
www.greatplay.com
Motor skills, fitness and coordination. Sport Birthday Parties, too. Motor skill programs for toddlers, pre-K and kindergarteners Athletic development program for grades k-5.

LEAPING LIZARDS
421 Boston Post Road
Port Chester, NY 10573
(914) 937-5867
Another indoor play space that is a good option for kids on a rainy day.

Bowling is another fun option for children and there are three large bowling alleys about 20-30 minutes from Greenwich:

AMF BOWLING CENTERS/AMF RIP VAN WINKLE LANES
701 Connecticut Avenue
Norwalk, CT 06854
(203) 838-7501
or at 47 Tarrytown Road
White Plains, NY 10607
(914) 948-2677
www.amfcenters.com

NEW ROCK BOWLING
33 Lecount Place
New Rochelle, NY 10801
(914) 636-3700

AMUSEMENT PARKS

LAKE COMPOUNCE THEME PARK
822 Lake Avenue
Bristol, CT 06010
(860) 583-3300
www.lakecompounce.com
Lake Compounce, Connecticut's biggest water park, is about 2 hours away from Greenwich so this outing requires some advance planning. Although there are a few rides for very young children, most of the fun is better for older children. Hours: The Park is open from May to October; hours vary from month to month.

RYE PLAYLAND
Playland Parkway
Rye, NY 10580
(914) 925-2701
www.ryeplayland.org
Another favorite in our house. Every time I go to Rye Playland I think of the movie BIG. This amusement park still has old-fashioned charm, along with many new rides for kids of all ages. It's especially nice that there are separate areas of the park, so that there are no older kids in the toddler area and vice versa. Rye Playland also has a swimming pool, beach, lake cruises, ice rink, and miniature golf.Hours: Open mid-May–September; hours vary from month to month.

ENTERTAINMENT

DOWNTOWN CABARET THEATER OF BRIDGEPORT
263 Golden Hill Street
Bridgeport, CT
(203) 576-1636
www.dtcab.com
This is another favorite in our household. We started going to the Downtown Children's Cabaret in Bridgeport soon after we moved to Greenwich in 2000 and we've seen every production since. The company does musical versions of classic stories and adds a humorous twist that makes the shows entertaining for parents too. Two performances on Saturdays and Sundays between September and May (they generally do 5 shows during the season).

GREENWICH HIGH SCHOOL BANDS
Greenwich High School
10 Hillside Road
Greenwich, CT 06830
203-625-8000
Concert Band, Symphony Band, Wind Ensemble, Jazz Ensemble.

GREENWICH PUBLIC SCHOOLS HONOR CHOIR

Concerts are listed on the Greenwich Public Schools Music Calendar. Admission is free to all their concerts.

GREENWICH HIGH SCHOOL THEATER ARTS

Greenwich High School
10 Hillside Rd.
Greenwich 06830
The GHS Theater Arts program is known throughout the state for the quality and diversity of its theatrical offerings. In April 2005, the Educational Theater Association recognized it as being one of the top five programs in the nation.

GREENWICH HIGH SCHOOL ORCHESTRA

Greenwich High School
10 Hillside Road
Greenwich, CT 06830
203-625-8000
Orchestra Director: Ms. Pat Harada

For information on what's going on at GHS and/or to purchase tickets, go to **www.greenwichschools.org** and select the Academics tab under Greenwich High School. Music and Theater Arts are some of the options and have show and ticket information.

NEW VICTORY THEATER

229 West 42nd Street
New York, NY 10036-7299
(646) 223-3020
www.newvictory.org
The New Victory Theater is a theater dedicated to kids and families. The theater presents very high quality theater, dance, music, vaudeville, puppetry and circus arts from around the world.

THE GREENWICH SYMPHONY ORCHESTRA

David Gilbert, Music Director
& Conductor
(203) 869-2664
Greenwich High School
Dickerman Hollister Auditorium
10 Hillside Road
Greenwich, CT 06830
203-625-8000
In its 48th Season, the Orchestra's 90-member professional orchestra brings a wealth of great music to our area.

THE LITTLE ORCHESTRA SOCIETY

Located at:
The Kaye Playhouse at Hunter College
East 68th Street
between Park & Lexington Avenues
(212) 971-9500
www.littleorchestra.org
The Little Orchestra Society presents unusual, dynamic concerts that make music more accessible and fun through interactive explorations, providing music in context, and thematic programming that educates and inspires.

THE PERFORMING ARTS CENTER— PURCHASE COLLEGE

735 Anderson Hill Road
Purchase, NY 10577-0140
(914) 251-6200
www.artscenter.org
SUNY Purchase's Performing Arts Center is only about 20 minutes from Greenwich and often has interesting performances for children. Call for schedule.

PURPLE COW CHILDREN'S THEATRE

200 Strawberry Hill Avenue
Stamford, CT (on the campus of
Sacred Heart Academy)
(203) 359-4414
www.stamfordtheatreworks.org
The Stamford Theater Works (STW)
Purple Cow Children's Theatre has
children's shows, from music to
puppets, during the months of May,
June, and July. Performances are on
Saturdays at 10 A.M. and 1 P.M., and
run about 45 minutes to an hour.

STAMFORD CENTER FOR THE ARTS

Rich Forum/Palace Theater
307 Atlantic Street
Stamford, CT 06901
(203) 325-4466
www.stamfordcenterforthearts.org
In winter, the Rich Forum in
Stamford puts on a performance
of The Nutcracker. While it is not the
New York City Ballet it is always a
lovely performance—and a lot cheap-
er than its New York City counterpart.
The Center also has many other performances, for children and adults.

WESTPORT COUNTY PLAYHOUSE

25 Powers Court
Westport, CT 06880
(203) 227-4177
www.westportplayhouse.org
Well-known and respected for its
productions for adults, the Westport
County Playhouse also offers plays
and puppet shows for children.

If you are searching for some
inexpensive local entertainment,
every Spring and Summer, there are
several school and church fairs which
are a lot of fun for children.
There are rides, games, live music,
and food. St. Paul's Church in
Riverside holds their Fair the first
weekend after Memorial Day.
St. Catherine's Church holds a fair
in mid-August and the North Mianus
School has a fair the first weekend
in May. There are fairs at the Cos Cob
and Glenville Elementary Schools too.
Check the local paper or look out for
signs on the road when you drive
around town.

Another fun annual event to attend is
Puttin' On the Dog, held in September.
It's a fun dog show held to raise
funds for *Adopt-a-Dog*. It's also a
great place to find a family pet!

As my children get older, I feel like
I should expose them to the variety
of cultures that surround us. I enjoy
taking them to places like Chinatown,
Little Italy or Arthur Avenue (the
Little Italy of the Bronx), Little India
(in New York City or Queens) so they
can truly experience different
cultures. And it's always fun to have
an authentic meal in any one of
these places!

NOTES

Chapter 5

ALL THINGS SPORT

Greenwich abounds in opportunities and places for kids to play sports. When you begin looking into sports programs for your children, your first stops should be the five places listed below. And that's just for starters.

GREENWICH BOYS AND GIRLS CLUB
4 Horseneck Lane
Greenwich, CT 06830
(203) 869-3224
www.bgcg.org

GREENWICH DEPARTMENT OF PARKS AND RECREATION
101 Field Point Road
P.O. Box 2540
Greenwich, CT 06836
(203) 622-7830
www.greenwichct.org

GREENWICH YMCA
50 East Putnam Avenue
Greenwich, CT 06830

(203) 869-1630
www.gwymca.org

GREENWICH YWCA
259 East Putnam Avenue
Greenwich, CT 06830
(203) 869-6501
www.ywcagreenwich.org

OLD GREENWICH-RIVERSIDE COMMUNITY CENTER (OGRCC)
90 Harding Road
Old Greenwich, CT 06870
(203) 637-3659
www.ogrcc.com

BASEBALL

The **BABE RUTH LEAGUE** is a non-profit organization sponsoring children ages 10–18.
For information, contact:
Vinnie Gullotta—Bambino Division
(ages 10–12) (203) 869-4132
Tina Carlucci—Junior Division
(ages 13–15) (203) 531-9223
Bob Spaeth—Senior Division
(ages 16–18)(203) 661-2386

For beginners in grades K–2, the **COS COB ATHLETIC CLUB** offers spring coed T-ball. For information, contact Toni Natale at (203) 869-0281.

GREENWICH DEPARTMENT OF PARKS AND RECREATION
101 Field Point Road
P.O. Box 2540
Greenwich, CT 06836
(203) 622-7830
www.greenwichct.org
Offering various baseball programs including Doyle Baseball/Softball School, Indoor Baseball, T-Ball, Small Fry Baseball, Midget Baseball, All Pro Sports Academy, Co-ed Baseball and summer programs as well.

OLD GREENWICH-RIVERSIDE COMMUNITY CENTER (OGRCC)
90 Harding Road
Old Greenwich, CT 06870
(203) 637-3659
www.ogrcc.com
Offering INTERMEDIATE LEAGUE (Grades 1-2), NATIONAL LEAGUE (Grades 3-4) and AMERICAN LEAGUE (Grades 5-up to 13). They also offer pitching clinics and hitting clinics, as well as a summer league for younger kids.

BASKETBALL

The **YMCA** has basketball clinics for children in grades 1–5.

The **GREENWICH DEPARTMENT OF PARKS AND RECREATION** has both coed and girls-only basketball for grades K–6.

The **GREENWICH BASKETBALL ASSOCIATION** has an instructional and competitive basketball program for grades 5–10.
Joe Curreri at (203) 661-4641

For boys in grades K-8, **G.O.A.T GEAR** has a basketball league located at Greenwich Catholic School, at 471 North Street. For information, contact Joe Jackson at (203) 651-4477.

FENCING

There is a fencing academy in Westchester which has a very good reputation. They have after school programs and private lessons as well as summer camps.

FENCING ACADEMY OF WESTCHESTER
40 Saw Mill River Road
Hawthorne, NY 10532
(914) 345-5005
www.fencewestchester.com

FIELD HOCKEY

The **GREENWICH DEPARTMENT OF PARKS AND RECREATION** has a field hockey club program. See listing above for contact information.

FOOTBALL

The **COS COB ATHLETIC CLUB** offers football practice for children ages 8–13. For further information, contact Vinnie Gullotta – Bambino Division (203) 629-2347, Kenny Herman – Junior Division (203) 698-0542, and Bob Spaeth – Senior Division (203) 637-8893.

GREENWICH YOUTH FOOTBALL LEAGUE has an instructional/competitive tackle football league for children ages 8–13.
For information, contact Will Dunster at (203) 625-0842 or go to www.greenwichfootball.com.

GOLF

For all the future golf pros, it is possible to take golf lessons. The following offer lessons for children and adults.

STERLING FARMS
1349 Newfield Avenue
Stamford, CT
(203) 461-9090
www.sterlingfarmsgc.com

GOLF TRAINING CENTER
Norwalk, CT
(203) 847-8008
www.golftraining.com

GYMNASTICS

For younger children, **TUMBLE BUGS** and **JACK RABBITS** are very popular for gymnastics.

TUMBLE BUGS
6 Riverside Avenue
Riverside, CT 06878
(203) 637-3303
Tumble Bugs, like Dance Adventure, is a fixture in the Greenwich area. Their gymnastics classes for children ages 18 months to 6 years are extremely popular. And like Dance Adventure, they also host birthday parties, which are great for children 3 to 5 years old, especially in winter when kids need a place to run around.

JACK RABBITS GYMNASTICS CLUB
397 Round Hill Road
Greenwich, CT 06831
(203) 622-0004
Jack Rabbits was created by former instructors at Tumble Bugs. The format is similar to Tumble Bugs.

MY GYM
225 Atlantic St.
Stamford, CT 06901
(203) 327-3496
www.my-gym.com
For children 3 mos. thru 13 yrs. My Gym offers gymnastics and movement classes.

For more serious young gymnasts, two places are recommended:

ARENA GYMNASTICS, INC.
911 Hope Street
Stamford, CT 06907
(203) 357-8167
www.arenagymnastics-ct.com

DARIEN YMCA
2420 Post Road
Darien, CT 06820
(203) 655-4584
www.darien-ymca.org

ICE HOCKEY

THE GREENWICH DEPARTMENT OF PARKS AND RECREATION sponsors ice hockey at the Dorothy Hamill Skating Rink for children ages 6 and up—there are even Adult Ice Hockey Clinics. In the fall, the Parks Department sponsors field hockey. The Boys and Girls Club of Greenwich also offers ice hockey.

GREENWICH BLUES YOUTH ICE HOCKEY ASSOCIATION
P.O. Box 1107
Greenwich, CT 06836
www.greenwichblues.com
For registration information, e-mail joebast@optonline.net.
Competitive, traveling ice-hockey teams for boys and girls.

GREENWICH SKATING CLUB
Cardinal Road
Greenwich, CT 06830
(203) 622-9583
www.greenwichskatingclub.com
A private skating club where children can skate or play hockey. One has to be sponsored to become a member and there are annual membership dues, but this is definitely worthwhile, especially for teenagers.

THE DARIEN ICE RINK is another reputable place for ice hockey instruction and practice. The rink also offers a hockey camp in summer and figure skating programs in the winter for children and adults.

DARIEN ICE RINK
55 Old Kings Highway North
Darien, CT 06820
(203) 655-8251

STAMFORD TWIN RINKS
1063 Hope Street
Stamford, CT 06907
(203) 968-9000
www.stamfordtwinrinks.com
Fall and spring hockey practice at this ice rink.

ICE SKATING

DOROTHY HAMILL SKATING RINK
Sherman Avenue
Greenwich, CT
(203) 531-8560
Skating sessions are open to the public at the Dorothy Hamill Skating Rink (yes, Dorothy Hamill spent most of her childhood in Riverside, CT), and you'll find private and group lessons here for children ages 4–16+. Call for additional information about programs, or call the the Greenwich Department of Parks and Recreation at (203) 622-7830.

DARIEN ICE RINK
55 Old Kings Highway North
Darien, CT 06820
(203) 655-8251

GREENWICH BOYS AND GIRLS CLUB
4 Horseneck Lane
Greenwich, CT 06830
(203) 869-3224
www.bgcg.org
Ice skating lessons and family skating.

GREENWICH SKATING CLUB
Cardinal Road
Greenwich, CT 06830
(203) 622-9583
www.greenwichskating.com
The Greenwich Skating Club is a good place for kids to skate or just hang out, although you need to

be a member.

STAMFORD TWIN RINKS
1063 Hope Street
Stamford, CT 06907
(203) 968-9000
www.stamfordtwinrinks.com
Ice skating instruction and open
skating sessions.

HORSEBACK RIDING

There are so many farms in the
Greenwich area that several offer
horseback riding lessons:

ARCADIA FARM
69 Stone Hill Road
Bedford, NY
(914) 234-6706

GREENWICH PONY CLUB
Contact: Megan Skakel
(203) 661-6878

KELSEY FARM
1016 Lake Avenue
Greenwich, CT 06831
(203) 869-5595
Kelsey Farm is a highly regarded
stable, known to have docile horses,
good instructors, and safe conditions
for children.

LIONSHARE FARM
404 Taconic Road
Greenwich, CT 06831
(203) 869-4649

PEGASUS THERAPEUTIC RIDING PROGRAM
45 Church Street, suite 205
Stamford CT 06905
(203) 356-9504
Pegasus Therapeutic Riding is a riding
program for people with disabilities.

WINDSWEPT FARMS
107 June Road
Stamford, CT
(203) 322-4984

MARTIAL ARTS

**THE CHINESE LANGUAGE SCHOOL
OF CONNECTICUT**
P.O. Box 515
Riverside, CT 06878
(866) 301-4906
www.chineselanguageschool.org

DEVITA KARATE
37 West Putnam Avenue
Greenwich, CT 06830
(203) 629-2467

**DYNAMIC MARTIAL ARTS FAMILY CENTER
OF GREENWICH**
202 Field Point Road
Greenwich, CT 06830
(203) 629-4666
www.westportkarate.com

KANG TAE KWON DO & HAPKIDO
263 Sound Beach Avenue
Old Greenwich, CT 06870
(203) 637-7867
www.kangmartialarts.com

OLD GREENWICH KARATE
242 Sound Beach Avenue
Old Greenwich, CT 06870
(203) 637-2685
www.bestkarate.org

SHIDOGAKUIN LTD.
38 Mary Lane
Greenwich, CT 06830
(203) 637-5475

WHITE TIGER TAE KWON DO
181 Greenwich Avenue
Greenwich, CT 06830
(203) 661-6054

LACROSSE

The Greenwich Youth Lacrosse organization sponsors lacrosse teams for children in grades 1 through 8:

GREENWICH YOUTH LACROSSE
P.O. Box 4627
Greenwich, CT 06831
(203) 352-3933
www.greenwichyouth-lacross.org

For boys and girls in grades K-8, the **TOP SHOTT** lacrosse organization has lacrosses leagues and clinics. The clinics are held at the Greenwich Catholic School, 471 North Street. For information, contact Pat Jackson at (201) 689-9155.

ARMONK INDOOR SPORTS CENTER
205 Business Park Drive
Armonk, NY
(914) 273-8522
www.armonkindoor.com

ROWING

GREENWICH WATER CLUB
49 River Road
Cos Cob, CT 06807
(203) 661-4033
www.greenwichwaterclub.com

The Greenwich Water Club is a new all-season recreational facility offering rowing, boating, an outdoor swimming pool and a fitness center.

SAILING

GREENWICH COMMUNITY SAILING
P.O. Box 195
Old Greenwich, CT 06870
(203) 698-0599
www.greenwichsailing.com
If you're interested in sailing lessons for yourself or your child, your first stop should be Greenwich Community Sailing at the Old Greenwich Yacht Club. There's a junior program for children ages 9–16 and an adult program for those over 17.

The Indian Harbor Yacht Club has a sailing program open to the public:

INDIAN HARBOR YACHT CLUB
710 Steamboat Road
Greenwich, CT 06830
(203) 869-2484
www.indianharboryc.com

If you're willing to travel a little farther, John Kantor's **LONGSHORE SAILING SCHOOL** in Westport is an excellent place for sailing lessons:

JOHN KANTOR'S LONGSHORE SAILING SCHOOL
Longshore Park
260 South Compo Road
Westport, CT
(203) 226-4646
www.longshoresailingschool.com

NORWALK SAILING SCHOOL
50 Calf Pasture Beach Road
Norwalk, CT

(203) 852-1857
www.norwalksailingschool.org

OFFSHORE SAILING SCHOOL
Washington Boulevard
Stamford, CT
(941) 454-1700
SOUND SAILING CENTER

54/A Calf Pasture Beach Road
Norwalk, CT 06855
(203) 838-1110
www.soundsailingcenter.com

SKIING

You can find several places to ski
within 90 minutes of Greenwich that
are perfect for small children. One
that is alright is **THUNDER RIDGE SKI
AREA** in Patterson, New York. It is a
very small mountain so it is perfect
for very small children. **THUNDER RIDGE**
has both ski school and private
lessons for children.

THUNDER RIDGE SKI AREA
P.O. Box 627
Route 22 & Birch Hill Road
Patterson, NY 12563
(845) 878-4100
www.thunderridgeski.com

A little further away but a much
better mountain is Mountain Creek
in New Jersey.

MOUNTAIN CREEK RESORT
200 Route 94
Vernon, NJ 07462
(973) 827-2000
www.mountaincreek.com

I would stress that **THUNDER RIDGE**
and **MOUNTAIN CREEK** are great for
small children but not so good for

experienced adult skiers because they
are very crowded and the slopes are
quite small.

If you are willing to travel a little
further for a long weekend, there are
several good ski areas within 3 hours
of Greenwich.

BUTTERNUT MOUNTAIN
380 State Road, Route 23
Great Barrington, MA 01230
(413) 528-2000
www.skibutternut.com

JIMINY PEAK THE MOUNTAIN RESORT
Hancock, MA.
(413) 738-5500
www.jiminypeak.com

MOUNT SNOW
46 Mountain Road
West Dover, VT 05356
(800) 245-SNOW
www.mountsnow.com

OKEMO MOUNTAIN
77 Okemo Ridge Road
Ludlow, VT 05149
(802) 228-4041
www.okemo.com

STOWE MOUNTAIN RESORT
89 Mountain Road
West Dover, VT 05356
1-800-253-4754
www.stowe.com

STRATTON MOUNTAIN
Stratton, Vermont
1-800-Stratton
www.stratton.com

SQUASH

Sometimes it seems that squash is the official sport of Greenwich, it's that popular. Two public courts, in addition to private clubs, are in the Greenwich vicinity:

SPORTSPLEX
49 Brownhouse Road
Stamford, CT
(203) 358-0066
www.sportsplex-ct.com

WESTCHESTER SQUASH
628 Fayette Avenue
Mamaroneck, NY 10543
(914) 698+0095
www.westchestersquash.com

SOCCER

The **GREENWICH DEPARTMENT OF PARKS AND RECREATION** sponsors soccer for children ages three-and-a-half to eight. Parents coach the "class" and the atmosphere is generally relaxed.

GREENWICH SOCCER CLUB
P.O. Box 383
Cos Cob, CT 06870
(203) 661-2620
anne@greenwichsoccer.com
This town-wide recreational program is for players in grades K–8 and is taught by parents.

OLD GREENWICH-RIVERSIDE COMMUNITY CENTER (OGRCC)
90 Harding Road
Old Greenwich, CT 06870
(203) 637-3659
www.ogrcc.com
The Old Greenwich Riverside

Community Center has soccer programs for children, as well as a **TRAVEL SOCCER LEAGUE.** Children who play on the Travel League are expected to make a minimum one-year commitment.

SOCCER WITH ALDWIN
21 First Street
Norwalk, CT 06851
(203) 857-4688
www.soccerwithaldwin.com
Another very popular soccer program.

For boys and girls ages 8 and up, there is yet another option:

GREENWICH TRAVEL SOCCER
This club is run by paid coaches and requires two practices a week and one game on Sunday. For more information on Travel Soccer, check www.greenwichtravelsoccer.com or contact Bob Giambo at rgiambo@optonline.net.

Armonk Indoor Sports Center also has soccer practice taught by instructors of the **FUTURE STARS SOCCER CAMP**, one of the better soccer camps in the area.

ARMONK INDOOR SPORTS CENTER
205 Business Park Drive
Armonk, NY
(914) 273-8522
www.armonkindoor.com

For serious soccer players, the premier soccer club is:

EASTERN NEW YORK SOCCER CLUB
53 North Park Ave.
Suite 207
Rockville Centre, N.Y.11570
(516) 766-0849
www.enysoccer.com

A new soccer league recently started in Norwalk. The **EVERTON SOCCER PARK** at All Saints School just opened the **COERVER SCHOOL**, a year-round soccer school to prepare boys and girls 4-10 years old for travel and premier soccer. For information, call (203) 966-8081.

SWIMMING

The first stop for swimming lessons and swim teams is the Greenwich **YWCA** or **YMCA**, but there are lots of other pools in the area.

GREENWICH BOYS AND GIRLS CLUB
4 Horseneck Lane
Greenwich, CT 06830
(203) 869-3224
www.bgcg.org
The Club recently built a new pool. They offer swimming lessons and a swim team to join.

PURCHASE COLLEGE
DIVISION OF PHYSICAL EDUCATION,
RECREATION & ATHLETICS
735 Anderson Hill Road
Purchase, NY 10577
(914) 251-5939
www.purchase.edu
SUNY Purchase's College Aquatics Program has children's group lessons and specialty programs.

SPORTSPLEX
49 Brownhouse Road
Stamford, CT
(203) 358-0066
www.sportsplex-ct.com
Private, semi-private, and group lessons for children.

JOAN LACLAIR SWIM SCHOOL
56 Sammis Street
Rowayton, CT
(203) 838-4848
The word is that this is a very good swimming program, run by Joan LaClair and taking place at the Doubletree Hotel in Norwalk. The drawback is that the classes are usually full, and difficult to get into.

If you have a swimming pool at home, there remains the option of asking one of the instructors or lifeguards at any of these pools to give your kids private lessons. For example, Jeff Cunningham Aquatics has great instructors:

JEFF CUNNINGHAM AQUATICS
private lessons
cunninghamaquatics@hotmail.com
(203) 273-2895
www.cunninghamaquatics.com

TABLE TENNIS

OLD GREENWICH-RIVERSIDE
COMMUNITY CENTER (OGRCC)
90 Harding Road
Old Greenwich, CT 06870
(203) 637-3659
www.ogrcc.com
The **AMERICAN YOUTH TABLE TENNIS ORGANIZATION** offers table tennis programs at the OGRCC.

TENNIS

In addition to both the **Y's** and the **Greenwich Department of Parks and Recreation**, the following places have tennis lessons for children and adults.

GRAND SLAM AT BANKSVILLE ROAD
IVAN LENDL TENNIS CENTER
1 Bedford-Banksville Road
Bedford, NY
(914) 234-9206
www.grandslamtennisclub.com

GREENWICH RACQUET CLUB
1 River Road
Cos Cob, CT 06807
(203) 661-0606

OLD GREENWICH-RIVERSIDE
COMMUNITY CENTER (OGRCC)
90 Harding Road
Old Greenwich, CT 06870
(203) 637-3659
www.ogrcc.com
Offering various programs for
ages 3-4 and 5-13.

OLD GREENWICH TENNIS ACADEMY
151 Sound Beach Avenue
Old Greenwich, CT 06870
(203) 637-3398

SOUND SHORE INDOOR TENNIS
303 Boston Post Road
Port Chester, NY
(914) 939-1300

STAMFORD INDOOR TENNIS CLUB
23 Radio Place
Stamford, CT 06906
(203) 359-0601

If you live in back-country and are a
tennis fan, consider joining the Armonk
Tennis Club, with private lessons and
tennis clinics for children and adults.

ARMONK TENNIS CLUB
546 Bedford Road
Armonk, NY 10504
(914) 273-8124
www.armonktennis.com

ARMONK INDOOR SPORTS CENTER
205 Business Park Drive
Armonk, NY
(914) 273-8522
www.armonkindoor.com
Winter tennis lessons and clinics.

TRACK

GREENWICH TRACK CLUB
www.greenwichtrackclub.com
bill@greenwichtrackclub.com
(203) 861-6835
Track club open to young athletes in
grades 3 to 5.

OTHER WAYS TO FITNESS

FITNESS EDGE KIDZ CLUB
THE FITNESS EDGE
1333 East Putnam Avenue
Greenwich, CT 06830
www.fitnessedge.net
(800) NEW-EDGE
Provides fun, comprehensive exercise
programs for children from newborns
to age 18.

GO VERTICAL
727 Canal Street
Stamford, CT 06902
(203) 358-8767
www.govertical.com
A really fun thing to do with older
kids is indoor rock climbing. You learn
a skill and get a lot of exercise at the
same time. Go Vertical is the largest
climbing gym in the state.

The New York Sports Club in Stamford
now has a **SPORTS CLUB FOR KIDS.** They
have recreational athletic programs for
tots to teens. Call (203) 323-6611.

Chapter 6

SUMMER CAMPS

My kids have sampled a variety of camps in Greenwich, from the summer camp at their preschool to the ESF Summer Camp, the weekly programs at the Audubon Center, and tennis camp. I have found that, as children get older, they prefer to go to more specialized camps focusing on arts, science or a specific sport. I think this is a good thing because it enables children to start developing and pursuing specific interests.

Every year, **GREENWICH COMMUNITY ANSWERS** publishes a brochure which lists all the camps in the Greenwich area. It is a very useful resource to get your hands on!

DAY CAMPS

The Town of Greenwich offers "camperships"—scholarships that defray some or all of the cost of summer day camps. The **GREENWICH DEPARTMENT OF SOCIAL SERVICES** and the **GREENWICH DEPARTMENT OF PARKS AND RECREATION**, located in Town Hall, runs the program. For further information, call Alison Brush, Social Services, at (203) 622-3715 or the Department of Parks and Recreation at (203) 611-7830.

ALLEGRA THEATER ARTS SUMMER STOCK
37 West Putnam Avenue
Greenwich, CT 06830
(203) 629-9162.
Director: Claudia Fletcher DeVita.
Ages 7–teen. Jazz, tap, hip-hop, classical ballet, drama, improvisation,

costume creation, stage makeup, theater dialogue. Evening performance for each session.

ARCH STREET TEEN CENTER
100 Arch Street
Greenwich, CT 06830
(203) 629-5744
www.archstreet.org
Director: Kyle Silver
Entering grades 7–9
Activities include hands-on arts & crafts, graphic design, film and radio production, and field trips.

AUDUBON CENTER IN GREENWICH
613 Riversville Road
Greenwich, CT 06831
(203) 869-5272, ext. 224
www.greenwich.center.audubon.org
The **Audubon Summer Nature Day Camp** offers a choice of three themes for children entering grades K-5:
Aquatic Adventures – campers explore different freshwater habitats including Indian Spring Pond, Mead Lake, and the Byram River to learn about water and the creatures who live in it.
Predators! – campers explore different habitats to find out who's eating whom and discover how predators capture food and how their prey tries to avoid being eaten!
Fantastic Five: A Sensory Camp – campers learn how animals use their senses to survive, and get a chance to test out the limits of their own senses! For older children: **Outstanding Teens Training in Ecological Research**, grades 6-8. Campers have the opportunity to work with Audubon's senior naturalist and other guest experts to survey different wildlife populations and their links to different habitats.

BANKSVILLE COMMUNITY HOUSE SUMMER CAMP
12 Banksville Road
Greenwich, CT 06831
(203) 622-9597
Director: Joel Goldsholl.
Ages 6–14.
Arts and crafts, cooking, fishing, sports, games, swimming, beach days, barbecues, and day trips.

BARTLETT ARBORETUM CAMP FOR KIDS
151 Brookdale Road
Stamford, CT 06903
(203) 322-6971
www.bartlettarboretum.uconn.edu
Activities include exploring science and nature on the Bartlett's beautiful 90 acres. Campers participate in planting gardens, exploring the greenhouse, conducting science experiments and creating arts and crafts.

BOY SCOUTS OF AMERICA GREENWICH COUNCIL – SETON CUB SCOUT DAY CAMP
33 Mason Street
Greenwich, CT 06830
(203) 869-8424 ext.3001
Boys finishing grades 1–4.
No prior scouting experience necessary. Archery, arts and crafts, boating, canoeing, fishing, hikes, nature and ecology, Scout craft skills, sports and games. Held at the Ernest Thomson Seton Reservation.

BOYS AND GIRLS CLUB OF GREENWICH
Horseneck Lane
Greenwich, CT 06830
(203) 869-3224
www.bgcg.org
Director: Don Palmer
Ages 6–12. Archery, athletics, canoeing, crafts, nature studies, special events, and swimming. Held at Camp Simmons. Teen Camp,

ages 13–15. Athletics, crafts, field trips, beach trips, game room, special events, swimming.

BRUCE MUSEUM SUMMER WORKSHOPS
The Bruce Museum
1 Museum Drive
Greenwich, CT 06830
www.brucemuseum.org
Directors: Blythin Leggett and Juline Chevalier
Reservations: Anne Burns at (203) 869-0376
Living Along the Shore at Greenwich Point - Coed, ages 6–9 (must have completed first grade).
Woodland Indians - plant and animal identification and ecology with crafts, stories, and hands-on demonstrations.
Palettes, Brushes and Paint! At the Bruce Museum - Coed, ages 7-13 (must have completed second grade). The basics of painting; experimenting with a variety of paints and techniques to create your own works of art; landscape, still life, portraiture and mural painting.
Scholarships available for all programs. Guest passes required for nonresidents of Greenwich for access to Greenwich Point. Call 869-6786, Ext. 338 for information.

BRUNSWICK SCHOOL BASEBALL CAMP
100 Maher Avenue
Greenwich, CT 06830
(203) 625-5800
www.brunswickschool.org
Director: Steve Weber
Boys ages 6–12

BUSH-HOLLEY HISTORIC SITE
39 Strickland Road
Cos Cob, CT 06807
(203) 552-5329
www.hstg.org

Young Artists Camp - Designed for older children with an interest in working with a variety of art materials.
Summer History Camp - Each two-week session includes Colonial American Week and Art Colony Week, focusing on the history and art of the late 1700s. Coed, for children entering grades 2-4.

BYRAM ARCHIBALD NEIGHBORHOOD CENTER
289 Delavan Avenue
Greenwich, CT 06831
(203) 531-1522
Director: Bill Woodson

CAMP GAN ISRAEL
270 Lake Avenue
Greenwich, CT 06830
(203) 629-9059
www.campgan.com
Director: Mrs. Maryashie Deren
Camp Gan: ages 4–12. Sports, arts and crafts, horseback riding, swimming on site, tennis; kosher lunch and transportation available.
Mini-Gan Camp: ages 20 months–3 years. Gym, soccer, cooking, nature, art, dance, sports, swimming, petting zoo. Call for fees. Sibling discounts and scholarships available.

CAMP PELICAN
At Greenwich Catholic School
471 North Street
Greenwich, CT 06830
15 East Putnam Avenue, #3330
Greenwich, CT 06830
(203)622-6654
www.pelicandaycamp.com
Ages 3–13. Archery, arts and crafts, baseball, bowling, computers, horseback riding, soccer, swimming and tennis. Transportation included.

CAMP PLAYLAND
800 Ponus Ridge Road
New Canaan, CT
(203) 966-2937
Director: Gary Bloom
www.campplayland.com
Ages 3–12.
Camp facilities include three heated
pools, ball fields, pond for boating
and fishing, low rope course, multi-
purpose court area for basketball and
other sports, picnic pavilion, play
areas, areas for music, drama, arts and
crafts, and more. Off-site tennis
instruction is provided for older
campers available.

CAMP SUNBEAM
At Christ Church Nursery School
254 East Putnam Avenue
Greenwich, CT 06830
(203) 869-6600
www.christchurchgreenwich.com
Director: Donald Kyle
Registrar: Sally Herring
Ages 5–8.
A fun, living environment for children
of various socioeconomic and ethnic
backgrounds. Art, drama, music,
swimming, sports, field trips.
Scholarships available.

CARDINAL BASEBALL CAMP
At Greenwich High School
baseball field
10 Hillside Road
Greenwich, CT 06830
(203) 869-3736
Head Coach: Mike Mora
Coed, ages 7–13.

CENTER FOR CREATIVE MUSIC
29 Forest Avenue
Old Greenwich, CT 06870
(203) 637-7568
Director: Karen Polimeni

Creative piano lessons for
children ages 5-teen.

CHILDREN'S DAY SCHOOL
139 East Putnam Avenue
Greenwich, CT 06830
(203) 869-5395
Director: Maryann O'Rourke
Ages 3–7.
Art, cooking, creative movement,
music.

CONNECTICUT ALL-STAR LACROSSE CLINIC
At Greenwich Country Day School
Old Church Road
Greenwich, CT 06830
(203) 863-5675
Director: Peter Walmsley
Entering grades 2–8.
Lacrosse for beginner and intermedi-
ate players.

**CONNECTICUT CHILDREN'S MUSICAL
THEATER**
At Arch Street Teen Center
100 Arch Street
Greenwich, CT 06830
(203) 852-9275
Directors: Ledell and Don Mulvaney
Ages 8–13.
Create original musical based on a
folk tale. Script and song writing,
scenery and prop making, costume
development, theater games,
rehearsals. Performance for family
and friends.

CURTAIN CALL
1349 Newfield Avenue,
Stamford, CT
(203) 329-8207
www.curtaincallinc.com
Summer Stock Program:
Ages 11–16.
Creative Theater Workshop:
improvisation, character development

and physical expressiveness;
Musical Workshop: ensemble singing, solo work and dance from popular Broadway musicals.
Summer Stock Junior Program:
Ages 6–11. Comprehensive theatrical experience for children on how to prepare for a production. Program concludes with performance for family and friends.

DANCE ADVENTURE DAY CAMP
230 Mason Street
Greenwich, CT 06830
(203) 625-0930
www.danceadventure.com
Director: Nola Van Alstine
Ages 3–9.
Props, music, acting, makeup, art and dance.

EAGLE HILL SCHOOL STUDY SKILLS PROGRAMS
45 Glenville Road,
Greenwich, CT 06830
(203) 622-9240
www.eaglehillschool.org
Director: Tom Cone
Ages 6–12. A language-intensive instructional program for children not performing up to their potential or needing to improve specific academic skills. Ages 11–15. Intensive instruction in study habits, note-taking, outlining, research, test-taking strategies.

ESF SUMMER CAMPS
At Greenwich Academy
200 North Maple Avenue
Greenwich, CT 06830
(203) 869-4444
www.esfcamps.com
Director: Bill Rouse
Day Camp, ages 4–8.
Arts and crafts, swimming, sports, creative expression, dance, science/nature, wilderness and adventure, games, special events. **Senior Camp**, ages 9–15. Arts, carpentry, cooking, movie-making, magic, sports, swimming, science, theater, outdoor living skills. **Sports Camp**, ages 7–14. Baseball, basketball, Euro-team handball, golf, lacrosse, soccer, swimming, street/field hockey, tennis, touch football, track, and volleyball. Weekly clinics with college coaches. **ESF Tennis Camp**, ages 6–15. For beginner, intermediate, and advanced players.

FASTRACKIDS
27 Rye Ridge Plaza
Rye Brook, NY 10573
(914) 937-6977
www.fastrackids.com
Ages 3-7.
Interactive learning adventures with CD-Rom-based lessons in a variety of subject areas, such as astronomy, natural sciences, and creative literature.

FIRST CHURCH DAY CAMP
First Congregational Church
108 Sound Beach Avenue
Old Greenwich, CT 06870
(203) 637-5430
Director: Tim Holman
Ages 3–8.
Beach, arts, games, music, nature, cookouts, sports and more.

FIRST PRESBYTERIAN CHURCH NURSERY SCHOOL ART SCAMPERS
37 Lafayette Place
Greenwich, CT 06830
(203) 869-7782
Director: Patricia Briar Case
Ages 3–6. Arts activities, music and movement, water play, parents' visiting days, specials guests. Weekly themes.

FUTURE STARS SUMMER CAMPS
546 Bedford Road
Armonk, NY 10504
(914) 273-8500
www.fscamps.com
Directors: Bill Griffin and
Charlie Van Dercook
Ages 3 1/2 – 16
Future Stars, as in stars in sports,
offers a variety of sports training
camps.

GOATGEAR BASKETBALL CAMP
Greenwich Civic Center
90 Harding Road
Old Greenwich, CT 06870
(201) 652-4472
Director: Pat Jackson
Ages 5–15.

GRAND SLAM TENNIS CENTER
1 Bedford-Banksville Road
Bedford, N.Y.
(914) 234-9206
www.grandslamtennisclub.com
Ages 3 and up.
Instructional programs for all playing
levels. Half- or full-day weekly
sessions.

GREENWICH BASKETBALL ASSOCIATION SUMMER CLINIC
at Central Middle School
P.O. Box 27
Cos Cob, CT 06807
Director: Bob Haugen
Grades K–8.

GHS CHEERLEADING CAMP
Greenwich High School
Hillside Road
Greenwich, CT 06830
(203) 531-6183
Director: Mary Ann Catalano
Girls, grades 3–9

GREENWICH COMMUNITY SAILING
Old Greenwich Yacht Club
Greenwich Point Park
(203) 698-0599
www.greenwichsailing.com
Director: Brent Lochridge
Coed, ages 9–16.
Boating, sailing, kayaking courses,
introductory to advanced.

GREENWICH COUNTRY DAY SCHOOL SUMMER CAMP
Old Church Road
Greenwich, CT 06830
(203) 863-5600
www.gcds.net
Director: Joe Perry
Ages 4 and 5.
Swimming, arts and crafts, stories and
poems, music, rhythms, games.
Ages 6–11.
Swimming, arts and crafts, nature,
drama, sports, woodworking, comput-
ers, day trips, sailing for ages 10-11.
GCDS Sports Corner, ages 12–13.
Swimming, baseball/softball, basket-
ball, golf, lacrosse, orienteering, sail-
ing/kayaking, soccer, street hockey,
tennis, woodworking, and day trips.

GREENWICH DEPARTMENT OF PARKS AND RECREATION
Town Hall
101 Field Road
Greenwich, CT 06830
(203) 622-7830
www.greenwichct.org
Camp Kairphree, ages 5–12.
(203) 637-4583
Activities at Old Greenwich Civic
Center, 90 Harding Road, Old
Greenwich and Greenwich Point.
Art and Music Camp, ages 9-12.
(203) 618-7649
All Pro Sports Baseball Academy,
ages 7-12.

(203) 618-7649
Summer Soccer with Aldwin,
ages 4-12.
Summer Fun I & II, ages 6-13.
(203)618-7649
Future Stars Tennis Camp, ages 6–14.
(914) 273-8500
**Skatepark Ramp Camp and
Skatepark Pee Wee Clinics,**
ages 6-12.
(203) 622-7821
Parks & Rec Summer Sports Camp, ages
6-13.
(203) 622-6484

GREENWICH MUSIC
1200 East Putnam Avenue
Riverside, CT 06878
(203) 637-1119
www.greenwichmusic.com
Learn how to play in a rock band.
The band will give a live performance
and cut a CD.

**GREENWICH PUBLIC SCHOOLS
SUMMER PROGRAM**
www.greenwichschools.com
Contact Mary Mediate at
(203) 625-8057 or Mary Forde
at (203) 625-7466 with questions.
A newly redesigned summer school
program, designed for students in
Pre-K through Grade 5, the program
focuses on a **"WORLD OF DISCOVERY"**
which includes multi-disciplinary thematic units designed to stimulate creative thinking and advance students
in reading, writing and math. Middle
and high school students may select
from traditional courses and special
interest workshops.

**GREENWICH RACQUET CLUB TENNIS
AND SPORTS CAMP**
1 River Road
Cos Cob, CT 06807

(203) 661-0606
Tennis and sports camp for
children ages 4-13.

**GREENWICH SKATE PARK SUMMER
RAMP CAMP**
100 South Arch Street
Greenwich, CT 06830
(203) 496-9876
www.greenwichct.org
Director: Harry Lefflebine
Ages 6–12.

**GREENWICH YOUTH STAGE
SUMMER WORKSHOP**
Round Hill Community House
397 Round Hill Road
Greenwich, CT 06830
(914) 484-2605
Director: Chandra Lee Mann
Ages 9–16.
Introduction to professional performance techniques, the ability to focus
and speak before an audience and
work as part of a team resulting in
the production of a musical.

KARATE AND SPORTS CAMP
DeVita Karate Academy
37 West Putnam Avenue
Greenwich, CT 06830
(203)629-2467
www.devitakarate.com
Director: Joseph DeVita
Ages 5 1/2 –12.

KINDERMUSIK
23 Clark Street
Old Greenwich, CT 06870
(203) 637-0461
Director: Sayre Lukason
Newborns to age 7, music and
movement classes.

LONG RIDGE CAMP
478 Erskine Road
Stamford, CT 06903
(203) 322-0253
www.longridgecamp.com
A summer day camp for boys and girls ages 3-13, run by the Alswanger Family for 46 years. Expert swim instruction, baseball, basketball, soccer, arts & crafts, dance, drama, music, archery, nature and mini golf, special events, cookouts and more. 3 outdoor pools, ballfields, playgrounds, nature trails and indoor facilities. CT State certified.

MAGIC DANCE
Director: Audrey Appleby,
(203)622-0744
Ages 3–teen.
Dance, singing, and acting classes, that include pre-ballet, creative movement, jazz, hip-hop, ballroom, swing.

MARITIME AQUARIUM SUMMER CAMP
10 North Water Street
Norwalk, CT
(203)852-0700, ext.2206.
www.maritimeaquarium.org
Ages 6-15.

MEAD SCHOOL
1095 Riverbank Road
Stamford, CT
(203)595-9500
www.meadschool.org
Creative Summer, ages 6–16.
Program emphasizing visual, expressive and performing arts with drama, dance, musical theater, drawing and painting, filmmaking, video classes and creative writing.
Sunpiper Program, ages 2 1/2–7.
Creative expression in music, drama, art, and writing—and outdoors play.

OGTA TENNIS AND SAILING DAY CAMP
(With Greenwich Community Sailing, listed above)
Greenwich Point Park
(203) 698-0599

SANDPIPERS BEACH CAMP
Old Greenwich-Riverside Community Center (OGRCC)
90 Harding Road
Old Greenwich, CT 06870
(203)637-3659
www.ogrcc.com
Ages 3 (potty trained) to 10.
Arts and crafts, games, music, nature, and swimming. Located at Tod's Point, beach or guest pass required. OGRCC membership required.

STONE BARNS CENTER FOR FOOD AND AGRICULTURE
630 Bedford Road
Pocantico Hills, NY 10591
(914) 366-6200
www.stonebarnscenter.org
Stone Barns Center for Food and Agriculture is a beautiful non-profit farm, educational center and restaurant in Westchester County. Their mission is to demonstrate, teach and promote sustainable, community-based food production. The day camp is for children ages 5-14 and gives children the opportunity to see how the farm works and how food is grown.

SUNY AT PURCHASE SUMMER PROGRAMS
735 Anderson Hill Road
Purchase, N.Y.
(914) 251-6508
www.purchasecollege.edu
Performing and fine arts program for children ages 7–18.

**PUTNAM INDIAN FIELD SCHOOL
SUMMER PROGRAM**
101 Indian Field Road
Greenwich, CT 06830
(203) 661-4629
www.pifs.net
Ages 2 1/2–6.
Arts and crafts, music, gym,
nature study, water play.

RED CROSS OF GREENWICH - SAFETY TOWN
99 Indian Field Road
Greenwich, CT 06830
(203) 869-8444
www.greenwichredcross.org
For children entering any Greenwich
kindergarten. Classroom is set up with
community helpers (police, firemen,
etc.) covering various safety aspects.

RYE ARTS CENTER SUMMER PROGRAMS
51 Milton Road
Rye, N.Y.
(914)967-0700
www.ryeartscenter.org
Music School: Ages 2–teen.
Adventure in songs and dance geared
to particular age groups, including
jazz-blues workshop for teens.
Art School: Ages 4–teen. A variety
of programs focusing on painting,
musical theater production, working
with clay, drawing.

SAINT PAUL'S SUMMER CAMP
Saint Paul's Episcopal Church
200 Riverside Avenue
Riverside, CT 06878
(203) 637-2447
Program director: Toni Natale
Coed, ages 3-6.
Arts and crafts, music, sports, dance,
nature and environment, water play.

SILVERMINE GUILD ARTS CENTER
1037 Silvermine Road
New Canaan, CT
(203) 966-6668
(203) 966-9700
www.silvermineart.org
Juniors Art Camp - Ages 5-8.
Learning by smearing, stretching,
smudging and squeezing a variety
of materials.
Youth Art Camp - Ages 8-12.
Traditional painting and drawing
techniques.

SOUNDVIEW SPORTS CAMP
Manhattanville College
2900 Purchase Street
Purchase, N.Y.
(914)323-5400
www.soundviewsports.com
Director: Steve Moynahan
Ages 6-14.
Soccer, basketball, baseball, lacrosse,
field hockey, swimming, volleyball,
golf, tennis, flag football and
computer skills.

SOUNDWATERS
Cove Island Park,
1281 Cove Road
Stamford, CT
(203)323-1978
www.soundwaters.org
Director: Katrina Penn
Ages 5-14.
Study and exploration of the marine
habitats of the Long Island Sound.

**STAMFORD THEATER WORKS CHILDREN'S
PERFORMING ARTS CAMP**
200 Strawberry Hill Avenue
Stamford, CT
(203) 359-4414
www.stamfordtheatreworks.org
Producer-director: Steve Karp
Children entering grades 2–6. Acting,

singing, comedy, movement and mime.

STEPPING STONES MUSEUM FOR CHILDREN
303 West Avenue
Norwalk, CT
(203) 899-0606 ext.247
www.steppingstonesmuseum.org
One, two, and three-week sessions with a different theme each week.

TINY TOTS SUMMER CAMP
97 Riverside Avenue
Riverside, CT 06878
(203) 637-1398
Directors: Tony and Maureen Pastore
Ages 2 3/4 – 6.
Swimming, crafts, music, stories.

WHITBY SCHOOL SUMMER CAMPS
969 Lake Ave.
Greenwich, CT 06831
(203)869-8464
Ages 4–14. Sports camp, theater workshop, math & science workshop, arts & crafts activities.
*Due to construction work, Whitby School will not be holding a summer program in 2007.

WINDSWEPT FARM
107 June Road
Stamford, CT
(203) 322-4984
Manager: Jenny Hoover
Coed, ages 5–17.
Horseback riding, horse care, grooming, show preparation, stable management, and games.

YMCA OF GREENWICH DAY CAMPS
50 East Putnam Avenue
Greenwich, CT 06830
(203)869-3381
www.gwymca.org
Child care camp director:
Carmel Vannoni
Ages 4-14.

YWCA OF GREENWICH PRESCHOOL CAMP
259 East Putnam Avenue
Greenwich, CT 06830
(203) 869-6501 ext. 251
(kindergarten) and
ext. 221 (pre-k, 3-4)
www.ywcagreenwich.org
Director: Sue Wilder
Ages 2-5.

For teenagers ages 14-15, the Town of Greenwich Department of Social Services has a **YOUTH CONSERVATION PROJECT** which has supervised outdoor employment with pay at town facilities, parks and conservation areas. For information, contact Jocelyn Ness at (203) 622-3800.

SLEEP-AWAY CAMPS

If you are looking into summer sleepaway camps, a great directory is **www.mysummercamps.com**. They have a directory of summer camps throughout the United States and forums for discussion. Also, if your children are interested in basketball camps, **www.allhoops.com** has information on basketball camps throughout the United States.

BRANT LAKE CAMP
(boys' sports camp, located in
Upstate New York)
7586 State Route 8
Brant Lake, NY 12815-2256
(518) 494-2406
www.brantlake.com

CAMP MATOAKA
(summer camp for girls, ages 7-14,
located in Maine)
32 Lanes End
Natick, MA 01760
(800) 628-6252
www.matoaka.com

CAMP SCHODACK
(co-ed summer camp, ages 7-14,
located in Upstate New York)
400 Hillside Avenue, Suite 11
Needham, MA 02494
(781) 444-5520
(800) 851-1164
www.schodack.com

CAMP TACONIC
(co-ed summer camp, ages 7-16,
located in Massachusetts)
20 Glenwood Court
Tenafly, NJ 07670
(201) 871-2086
www.camptaconic.com

CAMP TAKAJO
(summer camp for boys, ages 7-15,
located in Maine)
34 Maple Avenue
Armonk, NY 10504
(914) 273-5020
www.takajo.com

CAMP WAH-NEE IN TORRINGTON, CT
(co-ed summer camp, ages 7-17,
located in Torrington, CT)
61 Bogart Avenue
Port Washington, NY 11050
www.wahnee.com
(516) 883-1285

CAMP VEGA
(summer camp for girls, located
in Maine)
P.O. Box 990244
Boston, MA 02199
(617) 424-9919
www.campvega.com

CAMP WINADU
(summer sports camp for boys located
in Massachusetts)
P.O. Box 880449
Boca Raton, FL 33488-0449
(800) 494-6238
info@campwinadu.com
www.campwinadu.com

JCWP YOUNG WRITERS INSTITUTE
SUMMER CAMP
(located in Fairfield, CT)
Fairfield University
Fax: 203.254.4131
Cwp@mail.fairfield.edu
www.cwpfairfield.org
For program times, costs, or an application, contact Ms. Christine Lawton
at (203) 254-4000, ext. 3124, or by
e-mail at clawton@mail.fairfield.edu.

LAUREL SOUTH CAMP IN MAINE
(co-ed summer camp, ages 7-15,
located in Maine)
P.O. Box 14130
Gainsville, FL 32604
(800) 327-3506
(352) 331-4600
www.camplaurelsouth.com
fun@camplaurelsouth.com

POINT O' PINES CAMP FOR GIRLS
*(summer camp for girls, located
in Upstate New York)*
7201 State Route 8
Brant Lake, NY 12815
(518) 494-3213
www.pointopines.com

ROAD'S END FARM
*(horsemanship camp for girls,
ages 8-16, located in New Hampshire)*
P.O. Box 197
Jackson Hill Road
Chesterfield, NH 03443
(603) 363-4900
www.roadsendfarm.com

TRIPP LAKE CAMP
*(summer camp for girls, ages 8-16,
located in Maine)*
34 Maple Ave
Armonk, NY 10504
(914) 273-4065
www.tripplakecamp.com

SPECIALTY CAMPS

WIDE WORLD CHILDREN'S CORNER
521 East Putnam Avenue
Greenwich, CT 06830
(203)629-5567
Director: Kay Yamamoto.
Bilingual day camp: Ages 2–6.
Bilingual (Japanese & English) & ESL
programs. American and Japanese
festivals, Olympic games, field trips.

For children and families with
diabetes in their lives:

RAINBOW CLUB
At Round Hill Community House
397 Round Hill Road
Greenwich, CT 06830
www.childrenwithdiabetes.com
Mailing address:
Box 356
North Oxford, MA 01537-0356.
Director: Mary Ellen Flaherty,
(508) 987-2056

BIBLE CAMPS

GREENWICH BAPTIST CHURCH
10 Indian Rock Lane
Greenwich, CT 06830
(203) 869-2437
www.greenwichbaptist.org

FIRST UNITED METHODIST CHURCH
59 East Putnam Avenue
Greenwich, CT 06830
(203) 629-9584

JAPANESE GOSPEL CHURCH
286 Delavan Avenue
Greenwich, CT 06831
(203) 531-6450

Chapter 7

PARTY CENTRAL

With all the kids in Greenwich, it follows that there is a growth industry in party planning, entertainment, and venues for children's parties. Whether you want to hire help for a party at home, or have it somewhere that you don't have to clean up afterward, you'll find something to entertain your child on his or her special day.

I must say that my all-time favorite birthday party did not involve any entertainment whatsoever. The theme was a car wash party and, included in the invitation, was a booklet with coupons good for a car wash, pizza and soda. The kids came with their favorite cars and, upon arrival, went through the car wash which was set up using a garden hose with holes in it. Then, each child was given a bucket and sponge and proceeded to wash his or her car. The kids had a blast!

DO-IT-ALL

These services can organize the entire party for you, or you can hire a specific character to entertain the kids (such as Barbie, Spiderman), or someone who does tricks (magicians, jugglers, face painting). They will either come to your house or to a space you rent (keep in mind that the YWCA has space to rent). All you need to worry about is the food and cake!

HOLLYWOOD POP GALLERY
372 Greenwich Avenue
Greenwich, CT 06830
(203) 622-4057

ALWAYS ENTERTAINING
16 Havermeyer Lane
Old Greenwich, CT 06870
(203) 698-7773
www.alwaysent.com

AT-HOME PARTY IDEAS

MUSICAL ENTERTAINMENT

Hiring a musical entertainer for a party is an iffy proposition. You never really know how qualified the performer is unless you've heard about him/her from someone else. Musical entertainers at parties seem to work best for children 2 and under. Here are four musicians whom I and many of my friends have found to be quite good.

GRAHAM CLARKE
(914) 914) 669-5843
www.grahamclarke.com
graham@grahamclarke.com

JEFFREY FRIEDBERG & THE BOSSY FROG BAND
(845) 358-1115
www.bossyfrog.com

COLORFUL KENNY
(914) 348-8764

BOBBY DOO WAH
(914) 366-8291

Also, if your child attends a music class, it is sometimes possible to ask the music teacher for that class to entertain.

ACTING & COOKING

LET'S COOK, LIMITED
1-888-695-COOK
www.littlecooks.com
At a "Little Cooks" birthday party, children learn how to measure, pour, mix and stir their own party foods (cookies, pizza, etc.). Let's Cook brings all the supplies and the kids do all the cooking.

An interesting idea for older children is a Mystery Party. Mystery and Mayhem Productions will send someone to your home to organize a Mystery & Mayhem theater party. They also offer other themes, such as Pirate Treasure Hunts or Tarot Card/Palm Leaf Readings.

MYSTERY & MAYHEM PRODUCTIONS
32 East 7th Street
New York, NY 10003
(212) 260-2295
www.mysteryandmayhem.com

PRINCESS TEA PARTIES BY EILEEN
(203) 532-0547
Eileen will come to your home with a selection of princess dresses, baubles and bangles and help dress the children, do arts and crafts projects with them, and then serve them "tea" and small sandwiches—very elegant! Girls love it!

STORIES IN MOTION
(203) 625-6225
A trained storyteller from Stories in Motion allows children to explore their favorite stories with live music, creative movement, art and song.

SCIENCE PARTIES

DINOSAURS ROCK
(800) 411-3466
www.dinosaursrock.com
Dinosaurs Rock has a variety of
party ideas for children interested in
minerals, fossils and dinosaurs. Two
of my children took an after-school
program with Dinosaurs Rock and
really enjoyed it! Every week they
came home with a new project that
was both stimulating and fun.

MAD SCIENCE OF FAIRFIELD COUNTY
1122 Broadbridge Avenue
Stratford, CT 06615
(203) 381-9754
www.madscience.org
If your child is a budding scientist,
Mad Science offers fun and exciting
science programs for children ages
3-12. Their birthday parties offer
hands-on science experiences for
children that are educational and fun.
In addition to their birthday parties,
Mad Science has many interactive
educational programs offered through
schools, libraries, summer camps, and
other children's organizations.

ANIMALS

CRITTER CARAVAN
(203) 922-1826
(203) 333-5689
crittercaravan@cs.com
Critter Caravan offers an array of
exotic animals for children to learn
about and touch.

PIED PIPER
(203) 431-8322
(914) 763-6925
www.piedpiperponyrides.com
Pied Piper Pony Rides offers pony
rides and petting zoos, which they
will bring to your house. Besides
ponies, they have mini-ducks, mini-
sheep, pygmy goats, chickens, bunnies, pot-belly pigs and goats. Pied
Piper does a great job with the kids,
who love both the pony rides and
animals (even though some kids may
be a bit tentative at first about
approaching them).

There are several other organizations
or people who do animal presentations. A good source of information is
www.critterplaces.com/directory/CT.html.
There are two other people I have
heard about:

One is **JUNGLE JIM** at **PARTY SAFARI**.
He can be reached at (203) 249-8878
or partysafari@optonline.net.
The other person who does
animal presentations is

CHRIS EVERS at ANIMAL EMBASSY.
He can be reached at (203) 655-5404
or www.animalembassy.com. Chris
recently did a presentation at my
daughter's 7th birthday party and I
must say that he was excellent! He
had a roomful of 7-year-olds and
some adults completely captivated.
I highly recommend him!

TRUCKS

FIRE TRUCKS
It's possible to get a fire truck from
your local fire station to come to your
house in exchange for a donation to
the fire station. The kids can examine
all the different gauges and buttons
and play with the hose.

ICE CREAM TRUCKS
Imagine, an ice-cream truck will come

to your house or designated location and the kids can choose whatever they'd like. Wright's Ice Cream is especially fun because he owns a vintage ice-cream truck. This tends to go over very big with the kids.

DOMINICK'S ICE CREAM: (914) 937-3212

WRIGHT'S ICE CREAM: (203) 254-8313

SPORTS

For soccer buffs, **Mickey Kydes Soccer Enterprises** will send someone to your home to organize soccer games, soccer-related games, tricks and gifts. For information, contact:

MICKEY KYDES SOCCER ENTERPRISES
(203) 852-6969
www.kydessoccer.com

Someone else who organizes soccer parties is **Aldwin**, who will come to your house and organize a great soccer party with loads of prizes for everyone. I attended a soccer party for my friend's son and all my kids had a blast! For information, contact Aldwin at (203) 857-4688.

BOUNCERS & INFLATABLES

If your child has a summer birthday, or if you have a really big house or backyard, you can rent a bouncer with balls for your child's party:

CRUISIN AMUSIN—BALLS AND BOUNCERS
4 Daniels Farm Road Pmb123
Trumbull, CT 06611
(203) 261-9157

NEW ENGLAND BOUNCE ABOUT, LLC
P.O. Box 802
Newtown, CT 06470

(203) 364-0078
bounceabout@gmail.com

SUPER FUN INFLATABLES
(203) 790-8034
www.superfuninflatables.com
The place to go for bouncy castles and inflatable slides.

OTHER IDEAS

WEE PARTY
Just Wee Two now creates parties for 2 and 3-year old children. Parties are conducted by Just Wee Two staff members and include musical activities, arts & crafts and playtime. For information, call (800) 404-2204.

DANNY MAGIC, LLC
Magic@DannyMagic.biz
www.DannyMagic.biz.
(800) 619-1897
(203) 929-5816

PARTY PLACES

ADVENTURE KIDS
16 Old Track Road
Greenwich, CT
(203) 861-2227
Adventure Kids is an indoor playspace for kids. They can explore, climb and bounce on all the equipment, an especially fun idea for kids with winter birthdays. It gives them a chance to run around and let all that pent-up energy out.

ALLEGRA DANCE STUDIO
37 West Putnam Avenue
Greenwich, CT 06830
(203) 629-9162
Like Dance Adventure, Allegra Dance Studio will organize ballet, jazz,

tap or hip-hop dance parties for your child.

AMF RIP VAN WINKLE LANES
701 Connecticut Avenue
Norwalk, CT 06854
(203) 838-7501
www.amfcenters.com
and
AMF RIP WHITE PLAINS LANES
47 Tarrytown Road
White Plains, NY 10607
(914) 948-2677
www.amfcenters.com
Bowling is always a fun idea for boys and girls.

THE AUDUBON SOCIETY OF GREENWICH
613 Riversville Road
Greenwich, CT 06831
(203) 869-5272
www.greenwich.center.audubon.org
For a birthday party at the Audubon Center, you can either rent the space and go on a seasonal nature walk with one of the naturalists at the Audubon or hire an animalist, such as Chris Evers, to come and talk to the kids.

AUX DELICES FINE FOODS
(203) 326-4540 Ext. 108
Aux Delices offers hands-on cooking parties for children ages 7 and up. They have three fun-filled menus to choose from and chocolate or vanilla home-style birthday cake, which is the best cake in town! (They'll also bring the party to you for an additional fee.)

BELLTOWN FIRE STATION
8 Dorlen Road
Stamford, Connecticut 06905
(203)323-0626
www.belltownfire.com
The Belltown Fire Station is a working fire station where you can have your child's birthday party. Children learn about the trucks and get to climb on them. In addition, there is a large party hall which one can rent for the party.

BUILD-A-BEAR WORKSHOP
The Westchester
125 Westchester Ave.
White Plains, NY 10601
(914)328-3939
www.buildabear.com
As the name suggests, children get to make a stuffed bear, make a birth certificate for the bear and bring it home in a special carrying case.

CHILLY BEAR
401 Greenwich Avenue
Greenwich, CT 06830
(203) 622-7115
www.chillybear.com
Chilly Bear will set up and organize paintball parties at your house.

THE CLEARVIEW GREENWICH TWIN CINEMA or **THE CLEARVIEW RYE RIDGE CINEMA** allow you to have parties in one of their theaters. You can bring any DVD you want and they will play it for you. This is another good idea for winter birthdays.
Call (908) 918-2001 or check out www.clearviewcinemas.com for more information.

DANCE ADVENTURE
230 Mason Street
Greenwich, CT
(203) 625-0930
www.danceadventure.com
Dance Adventure will create a variety of theme parties for children. Kids usually dance along to a story with piano accompaniment and do arts and

crafts projects. I especially recommend these parties for girls 5–8 who really enjoy ballet.

DIMARE'S PASTRY SHOP
12 Largo Drive South
Stamford, CT
(203) 967-2253
With DiMare's cookie-making parties, the children decorate the cookies they bake themselves and then bring them home. This is a fun and different party for kids, and is also good for children with winter birthdays... staying inside with an oven going is more fun in the winter!

Like Adventure Kids, Fun for Kids and Leaping Lizards have indoor play-spaces to have birthday parties:

FUN FOR KIDS & GROWNUPS TOO
370 West Main Street
Stamford, CT 06902
(203) 326-5656
www.fun4kidsarcade.com

KIDS 'R' COOKIN
(914) 937-2012
www.kidsrcookin.com

KIDS U
633 Hope Street
Stamford, CT 06907
(203) 358-9500
www.kids-u.com
Kids U was founded in 2003 and has both classes and kids' birthday parties. The gym parties include an hour of free play on the "play-quad" and supervised activities in the gym room. At their Norwalk location, they offer Glamour girls parties.

LAKESIDE POTTERY
543 Newfield Avenue
Stamford CT 06905
(203) 323-2222
www.lakesidepottery.com.

LEAPING LIZARDS
421 Boston Post Road
Port Chester, NY 10573
(914) 937-5867

THE LOEWS/AMC THEATER in Port Chester also offers birthday party packages. They even have a party room where you and your guests can have pizza and cake after the movie. They are at:
40 Westchester Avenue
Port Chester, NY 10573
(914) 510-1010
www.amctheaters.com

MICHAEL'S ARTS & CRAFTS in Port Chester has craft parties for kids. For information, call(914) 937-3060. They are located at 27 Waterfront Place, Port Chester, NY 10573.

MY GYM
225 Atlantic St.
Stamford, CT 06901
(203) 327-3496
www.my-gym.com
My Gym organizes celebrations created specifically for your child, with special song and game requests! Games, gymnastics, Space Flight, puppets, rides, songs and exciting birthday events led by the trained staff!

NEW CANAAN NATURE CENTER PARTY
144 Oenoke Ridge
New Canaan, CT 06840
(203) 966-9577
www.newcanaannature.org
Natural science birthday parties for

children ages 3–12. Learn and have fun at the same time. All you need to bring is the food and cake.

NORWALK AQUARIUM PARTIES
10 North Water Street
Norwalk, CT
(203) 852-0700 ext 2206
www.maritimeaquarium.org
Parties at the Norwalk Aquarium consist of a guided tour of the aquarium, and then a stop at the party room for cake and refreshments. The party finishes up with a paper craft activity or a guided trip into the aquarium's special exhibits and Maritime Hall.

You can also have a "Maritime Aquarium" birthday party in your home. A member of the Norwalk Aquarium staff will come to the party with your choice of a presentation— **"Sharks!"**; **"Whale Tales"**; or **"Crawling Critters."**

ROUTE 22 DONUT PARTY
55 Old Route 22
Armonk, NY 10504
(914) 765-0022
www.route22restaurant.com
Route 22 is a 1930s-style American restaurant. They have donut-making parties for children. I recently had a birthday party there for my twins and I must say that the kids (and parents) had a great time. Because I had about 35 kids, I also hired a magician and that helped keep the party in control. Route 22 also does a lot of Bar/Bat Mitzvahs.

SHARKEY'S CUTS FOR KIDS
"GLAMOUR GIRL" PARTY
220 East Putnam Avenue
Cos Cob, CT 06807
(203) 629-KIDS

www.sharkeyscutsforkids.com
The party takes place in Sharkey's special **"Glamour Girl"** dressing room, where each little girl is pampered with a pretty hairstyle, makeup application, and mini-manicure. When they are all ready to go, the girls can choose from an array of beautiful dress-up clothes and put on a fashion show, where their picture is taken. I assure you, girls love this!

SPORTSPLEX BIRTHDAY PARTIES
Contact Rose Guitton at
(203) 358-0066 ext. 212.
www.sportsplex-ct.com
Sportsplex offers a variety of birthday parties:
Aqua Fun: Great for a party all year long in their 4-ft.-deep lap pool. The staff will organize a variety of age-appropriate water games and assist children with their swimming inside the pool. Ages 6 and up.
Basketball: With the help of an experienced instructor, the party prepares for a game by learning basic drills and classic moves.
Ages 5 and up.
Kids' Kickboxing: With a qualified instructor, children learn the time-honored techniques of the martial arts. Ages 5 and up.
Party Games: A back-to-basics party that is packed full of fun—relay races, dance the Limbo, musical chairs, ball play, freeze dance, and much more. Ages 4 and up.
Circus Fun: Kids spend an hour with a clown, learning to juggle, getting their faces painted, and playing lots of games.
Gymnastics Party: Kids get to spend an hour with an instructor learning to tumble and jump on all the equip-

ment. Ages 2 and up.

Squash Party: An instructor walks the children through a game of squash. Ages 6 and up.

Craft Party: The children make a wide range of different crafts. Ages 5 and up.

Make-a-Cake: The children pretend they are bakers and decorate cakes for the party. Ages 7 and up.

STEPPING STONES MUSEUM PARTIES
Matthews Park
303 West Avenue
Norwalk, CT 06850
www.steppingstonesmuseum.org
The Stepping Stones birthday package includes a guided birthday experience for children 4 years and older for up to 20 children. A Discovery Guide leads the kids around the museum, and then they do a craft activity, before going into the party room for refreshments and cake. Generally, the party takes place during regular museum hours. There is also the option of renting the whole museum for your child's party but that is expensive.

TED E. BEAR & FRIENDS FACTORY
1074 Hope Street, 2nd Floor
Stamford, CT 06907
(203) 461-8556
www.tedebearandfriendsfactory.com
Like Build-a-Bear Workshop, children get to stuff a bear and bring it home in a special case.

TUMBLE BUGS
6 Riverside Avenue
Riverside, CT 06878
(203) 637-3303
At this kids' gym, partygoers spend about an hour on all the equipment, play games organized by the staff, and then go into the party room for

pizza and cake. This is always a hit for children 3–4 years old, especially for those with winter birthdays when you'd just rather be inside.

WHIMSIES DOLLHOUSE & MINIATURE SHOP PARTY
18 Lewis Street
Greenwich, CT 06830
(203) 629-8024
Whimsies has cute birthday parties where children first do a small arts and crafts project then get to play with the beautiful dollhouses in the shop. Works best for a small group of older girls.

YOGA PARTIES AT YOGA SAMADHI
328 Pemberwick Road @ The Mill
Greenwich, CT 06831
(203) 532-0660
www.greenwichyoga.com
Each party begins with an imaginative one-hour yoga class with themes and props, led by a qualified instructor. This is followed by a half hour of refreshments in the studio.

CAKES & CATERERS

After several years of purchasing expensive cakes for my children, I realized that kids rarely eat more than the frosting! As a result, I now buy a box of cupcakes and put tons of frosting on each cupcake and the kids are thrilled! Plus, I don't find myself eating birthday cake for the next two weeks. Nonetheless, it's nice to have a beautiful cake once in a while, and for those occasions, there are many tried-and-true places to find them in the Greenwich area. Also listed below are a variety of caterers, in case you are looking to serve something other than pizza at your child's birthday party!

ARMONK BAGEL EMPORIUM
393 Main Street
Armonk, NY 10504
(914) 273-9111

AUX DELICES
1075 East Putnam Avenue
Riverside, CT 06878
(203) 698-1066
or
3 West Elm Street
Greenwich, CT 06830
(203) 622-6644

BALDUCCI'S
1050 East Putnam Avenue
Riverside, CT 06878
(203) 637-7600

BASKIN ROBBINS (Ice Cream Cakes)
146 Sound Beach Avenue
Old Greenwich, CT 06870
(203) 637-0480

BLACK FOREST PASTRY SHOP
52 Lewis Street
Greenwich, CT 06830
(203) 629-9330
www.sweetsomethings.com

DARLENE'S HEAVENLY DESIRES
185 Sound Beach Avenue
Old Greenwich, CT 06870
(203) 698-9441
A large selection of chocolates, candy, ice cream, and Coney Island Cream.

DIMARE'S PASTRY SHOP
Riverside Commons
Riverside, CT 06878
(203) 637-4781

GARDEN CATERING
177 Hamilton Avenue
Greenwich CT 06830
(203) 422-2555

185 1/2 Sound Beach Avenue
Old Greenwich CT 06870
(203) 637-7699
www.gardencatering.net

HAPPINESS IS BAKERY AND CAFÉ
1069 North Street
Greenwich, CT 06830
(203) 861-4020

PLUM PURE FOODS
236 East Putnam Avenue
Cos Cob, CT 06807
(203) 869-7586
www.plumpurefoods.com

SAINT MORITZ
383 Greenwich Avenue
Greenwich, CT 06830
(203) 869-2818

UPPER CRUST BAGEL CO.
197 Sound Beach Avenue
Old Greenwich, CT 06870
(203) 698-0079

SWEET LISA'S
3 Field Road
Cos Cob, CT 06807
(203) 869-9545
www.sweetlisas.com
Sweet Lisa's makes the most beautiful—and the most expensive—birthday cakes. Her cakes are always a hit!

SUPPLIES

For all those other things you're going to need for a birthday party: from tables and chairs to paper plates, cups, decorations, goodie bags, and party favors to fill them:

ADA'S VARIETY SHOP
112 Riverside Avenue
Riverside, CT 06878
(203) 637-0305
A Greenwich landmark, Ada's is
THE candy store of candy stores!

ANN'S HOBBY SHOP
405 East Putnam Avenue
Cos Cob, CT 06807
(203) 869-0969

DARLENE'S HEAVENLY DESIRES
185 Sound Beach Avenue
Old Greenwich, CT 06870
(203) 698-9441
A large selection of chocolates, candy,
ice cream, and Coney Island Cream.

EAST PUTNAM VARIETY
88 East Putnam Avenue
Greenwich, CT 06830
(203) 869-8789

GREENWICH PARTY BALLOONS
257 East Putnam Avenue
Cos Cob, CT 06807
(203) 625-8628

KATE'S PAPERIE
125 Greenwich Avenue
Greenwich, CT 06830
(203) 861-0025

MICHAEL'S ARTS & CRAFTS
27 Waterfront Place
Port Chester, NY 10573
(914) 937-3060

PACKAGES PLUS 'N MORE
215 East Putnam Avenue
Cos Cob, CT 06807
(203) 625-8130

THE PAPERY BY PAPYRUS
268 Greenwich Avenue
Greenwich, CT 06831
(203) 869-1888
www.thepapery.com
www.papyrusonline2.com

PARTY CITY
2255 Summer Street
Ridgeway Shopping Center
Stamford, CT 06805
(203) 964-4961
www.partycity.com

PARTY FIXINS
Havermeyer Lane
Old Greenwich, CT 06870
(203) 359-3922
www.partyfixins.com

PARTY PAPER AND THINGS INC.
410 East Putnam Avenue
Cos Cob, CT 06807
(203) 661-1355
Balloons, favors, wrapping papers,
greeting cards, pinatas, decorations.
They deliver!

NOTE ON PARTY FAVORS:

As the mother of four kids who
often get invited to the same
birthday parties, I feel I'm qualified to make a suggestion about
party favors. Although the usual
custom is to fill a goodie bag or
sand bucket with stickers, candy,
etc., consider a more educational
gift such as a book, Play-Doh, or
a board game. These items aren't
that much more expensive, but
they are certainly more meaning-
ful and will last longer.

SMITH PARTY RENTALS
133 Mason Street
Greenwich, CT 06830
(203) 869-9315
www.smithpartyrentals.com

SAINT-CLAIR STATIONERS & ENGRAVERS
23 Lewis Street
Greenwich, CT 06830
(203) 661-2927
www.theresesaintclair.com

STAMFORD TENT
84 Lenox Avenue
Stamford CT 06906
(203) 324-6222
www.stamfordtent.com
Only for tents.

STRAUSS WAREHOUSE OUTLET
140 Horton Avenue
Port Chester, NY
(914) 939-3544
www.straussoutlet.com

GIFTS

A.I. FRIEDMAN
431 Boston Post Rd
Port Chester, NY 10573
(914) 937-7351
www.aifriedman.com
Friedman's is an exceptionally good arts supply store with a great selection of arts and crafts educational gifts for children. (And if you're brave enough to make your child's Halloween costume, it's a good place to go for supplies.)

ANN'S HOBBY SHOP
405 East Putnam Avenue
Cos Cob, CT 06807
(203) 869-0963

DIANE'S BOOKS OF GREENWICH
8a Grigg Street
Greenwich, CT 06830
(203) 869-1515
www.dianesbooks.com
Wonderful selection of books for children and adults, and the well-read staff is always ready to help you find just the right book! Diane's Books occasionally has special book signings and events for kids.

GRAHAM'S KIDS CUTS
60 Greenwich Avenue
Greenwich, CT 06830
(203) 983-6800
Graham's Kids Cuts, besides being a fun place to get a haircut, sells educational and fun toys and books. The owner really makes an effort to get the best selection of toys— interesting blocks and board games.

JUST BOOKS
28 Arcadia Road
Old Greenwich, CT 06870
(203) 637-0707
www.justbooks.org
Besides a great selection of kids' books, Just Books also has book groups, book signings and special events for kids. In addition, the owner of Just Books (and Arcadia Coffee Shop) shows movies for kids.

MICHAEL'S ARTS & CRAFTS STORE
2233 Summer Street
Stamford, CT
(203) 978-0026
or
27 Waterfront Place
Port Chester, NY 10573
(914) 937-3060
www.michaels.com
Michael's is a good place to go for arts and crafts supplies and it also has a

small selection of gifts for children.

RINK AND RACQUET LTD.
24 Railroad Avenue
Greenwich, CT 06830
(203) 622-9180

SMART KIDS' TOYS
17 East Elm Street
Greenwich, CT 06830
(203) 869-0022
www.sktoys.com
A well-chosen selection of toys
for children of all ages—and
better quality than you'll find
at the national chain stores.

THE FUNHOUSE
236 Sound Beach Avenue
Old Greenwich, CT 06870
(203) 698-2402

WHIMSIES DOLLHOUSE &
MINIATURE SHOP
18 Lewis Street
Greenwich, CT 06830
(203) 629-8024
Whimsies has beautifully crafted
dollhouses and dollhouse supplies for
children. A gift that lasts a long time.

SPECIAL EVENTS

Bar/Bat Mitzvah's and Sweet Sixteen
celebrations are important milestones
in your child's life. Much research
goes into planning for this kind of
celebration. This is a start:

VENUES

BANK STREET EVENTS
65 Bank Street
Stamford, CT 06901

(203) 325-2739
www.bankstreetevents.com

CAPERBERRY EVENTS – C.V. RICH MANSION
52 Gedney Way
White Plains, NY 10605
(914) 949-3543
www.caperberryevents.com

THE CAPITOL THEATER
149 Westchester Avenue
Port Chester, NY 10573
(914) 934-9362
www.thecapitoltheatre.net

CASTLE ON THE HUDSON
400 Benedict Avenue
Tarrytown, NY 10581
(914) 524-6366
www.castleonthehudson.com

CLUB MOR
129 Atlantic Street
Stamford, CT 06901
(203) 357-7755
www.mornightlife.com

GLEN ISLAND HARBOUR CLUB
Glen Island Park
Weyman Avenue
New Rochelle, NY 10801
(914) 636-6500

MAMARONECK BEACH AND YACHT CLUB
555 South Barry Avenue
Mamaroneck, NY 10543
(914) 698-1130
www.mamaroneckbeachandyachtclub.com

WHITBY CASTLE
330 Boston Post Road
Rye, NY 10580
(914) 777-2053

In addition to the above, you can
also have parties at some of the

birthday party locations listed above, such as **AMF RIP VAN WINKLE LANES** or **THE MARITIME AQUARIUM**. You can also try the local hotels such as the **HYATT** or **DELAMAR** in Greenwich, or the **WESTIN** or **MARRIOTT** in Stamford.

FLOWERS AND DÉCOR

ARCADIA FLORAL CO.
411 Mamaroneck Avenue
Mamaroneck, NY 10543
(914) 777-2800
(800) ARCADIA
www.arcadiafloral.com

CAROLYN DEMPSEY DESIGN
189 1/2 North Main Street
Port Chester, NY 10573
(914) 937-7504

DANIEL FLORALS & EVENTS INC.
33 New Broad Street
Port Chester, NY 10573
(914) 374-8232
www.danielflowers.net

DIANA GOULD LTD.
12 Frontage Street
Elmsford, NY 10523
(914) 347-7134
(800) 959-6887
www.dianagouldltd.com

GRAND EVENTS EAST LLC
18 Arcadia Road
Old Greenwich, CT 06870
(203) 223-0756
(203) 698-1461
www.grandeventseast.com

X-QUISITE FLOWERS & EVENTS INC.
520 North Avenue
New Rochelle, NY 10801
(914) 632-8700
www.xquisitevents.com

ENTERTAINMENT

BIG DADDY'S RACING
865 Beckley Road
East Berlin, CT 06023
(860) 655-8226
www.bigdaddysracing.net

HAL PRINCE MUSIC & HPM DJS
111 Bowman Avenue
Rye Brook, NY 10573
(203) 324-0700
(914) 937-4700
www.hpmdjs.com

JAMES DANIEL MUSIC & ENTERTAINMENT
125 Bedford Street
Stamford, CT 06901
(203) 969-2400
www.jamesdaniel.com

JIMMY DEE MUSIC PRODUCTIONS
195 East Post Road
White Plains, NY 10601
(914) 428-9231
www.jimmydee.com

KLEZMER BY ALICIA SVIGLAS
(877) KLEZMER
www.aliciasvigals.com

THE MAIN EVENT
(800) 427-6359
(718) 724-1007
www.themaineventonline.com

NY PARTY WORKS
130 Dale Street
West Babylon, NY 11704
(631) 501-1414
(800) 4NY-FUNN
www.nypartyworks.com

TOTAL ENTERTAINMENT
123 Liberty Street
Danvers, MA 01923

(888) 339-9995
(978) 777-2050
www.totalentertainment.biz

YAHNEY ENTERTAINMENT GROUP/
DJ JEFF YAHNEY
Dix Hills, NY 11746
(800) SAY-JEFF
(631) 425-JEFF
www.sayjeff.com

PHOTOGRAPHERS

DÉJÀ VU STUDIOS
1 Stamford Plaza
Stamford, CT 06901
(914) 925-7700
and
350 Theodore Fremd Avenue
Suite 300
Rye, NY 10580
(914) 725-7700

FANTASY FLASH PHOTOGRAPHY &
VIDEO SERVICES
195 East Post Road
White Plains, NY 10601
(914) 428-9231
(914) 328-0001
www.jimmydee.com

STUDIO A IMAGES PHOTO &
VIDEO PRODUCTIONS
418 East Putnam Avenue
Greenwich, CT 06807
(203) 661-3393

VIDELER PHOTOGRAPHY
138 South Compo Road
Westport, CT 06880
(203) 226-9223
www.videler.com

GIFTS AND PARTY FAVORS

THE ACTIVE EDGE CLOTHING COMPANY
(800) 343-1497
www.theactiveedge.com

THE IMAGE MAKERS
79 St. John's Avenue
Yonkers, NY 10704
(914) 963-8551
www.theimage-makers.net

EDIBLE IMPRINTS
143A South Prospect Avenue
Bergenfield, NJ 07621
(201) 384-2279
www.edibleimprints.com

THE HAMPTON POPCORN COMPANY
(914) 305-4736
www.hamptonpopcorn.com

THE MAIN EVENT
(800) 427-6359
www.themaineventonline.com

For more information on planning a
Bar/Bat Mitzvah, **www.mitzvahchic.com**
is a great resource. There is also a
Bar/Bat Mitzvah Party Guide that
comes out every year. For information,
call (718) 615-2500. Every year, there
is a party showcase called **Celebrate!**
Party Showcases. For a list of dates,
call (203) 322-2840 or visit
www.celebratepartyshowcase.com.

Chapter 8

CHILD STYLE

When it comes to child style, Greenwich is definitely the place to be! There is no dearth of cute clothing stores, hairdressers, and photographers. On Greenwich Avenue alone, there are eight kids' clothing stores, at least two portrait photographers, and two hairdressers for kids. So, whether your child's style is more formal or more casual, you'll be able to find something great in town.

CLOTHING

ANNA BANANA BY HOAGLAND'S
248 Sound Beach Avenue
Old Greenwich, CT 06870
(203) 637-0128

BEST & CO.
289 Greenwich Avenue
Greenwich, CT 06830
(203) 629-1743

BROOKS BROTHERS
181 Greenwich Avenue
Greenwich, CT 06830
(203) 863-9288

CANDY NICHOLS
59 Purchase Street #B
Rye, NY 10580
(914) 967-2288
or
67 Elm Street
New Canaan, CT 06840
(203) 972-8600

GAP KIDS
264 Greenwich Avenue
Greenwich, CT 06830
(203) 625-0662

HOAGLAND'S OF GREENWICH
175 Greenwich Avenue
Greenwich, CT 06830
(203) 869-2127

L'ENFANCE MAGIQUE
365 Greenwich Avenue
Greenwich, CT 06830
(203) 625-0925

LOVE
22 West Putnam Avenue
Greenwich, CT 06830
(203) 422-0900
www.shopwithlove.net
Love is a new children's lifestyle
store in Greenwich.The owner
carries adorable things for children.

PETIT BATEAU
84 Greenwich Avenue
Greenwich, CT 06830
(203) 622-8300

PETIT PATAPON
271 Greenwich Avenue
Greenwich CT 06830
(203) 861-2037

WISH LIST
350 Greenwich Avenue
Greenwich, CT 06830
(203) 629-4600

For children's **eyewear**, check out:

20/20 KIDS
15 Arcadia Road
Old Greenwich, CT
(203) 698-2255

A fun, inviting, stress-free environment in which young people can
choose eye glasses, 20/20 Kids is
the only optical store tailored
exclusively for youngsters in
Connecticut. They showcase twenty
designers and carry a wide variety of
eye glasses for kids.

If you are looking for **shoes**, the
three stores listed below have a large
selection of children's shoes:

LITTLE ERIC OF GREENWICH
15 East Elm Street
Greenwich, CT 06830
(203) 622-1600

SHOES 'N MORE
251 Greenwich Avenue
Greenwich, CT 06830
(203) 629-2323
or
9 South Avenue
New Canaan, CT 06840
(203) 972-8484

PLAZA BOOTERY
360 Greenwich Avenue
Greenwich, CT 06830
(203) 622-5088

For gymnastics, ice-skating, or
dancewear, Beam and Barre has
everything you could possibly need:

BEAM AND BARRE
352 Greenwich Avenue
Greenwich, CT 06830
(203) 622-0591

For sports uniforms and equipment, your best bets are:

ALL-SPORTS APPAREL
146 Sound Beach Avenue
Old Greenwich, CT 06870
(203) 698-3055

ASF PROMOTIONS
551 East Putnam Avenue
Cos Cob, CT 06807
(203) 629-1808

BRUCE PARK SPORTS
104 Mason Street
Greenwich, CT 06830
(203) 869-1382

RINK & RACQUET LTD.
24 Railroad Avenue
Greenwich, CT 06830
(203) 622-9180

THREADS & TREADS
17 E Putnam Avenue
Greenwich, CT 06830
(203) 661-0142

HAIRCUTS

GRAHAM'S
60 Greenwich Avenue
Greenwich, CT 06830
Tel.: (203) 983-6800
graham@grahamskidscuts.com
Graham's opened in the summer of 2002. They do what they can to make your child's haircut a happy moment! My kids love going there.
As mentioned in chapter 7, the shop also sells great toys and books.

SNIPS-SNAPS
1051 Long Ridge Road
Stamford, CT 06903
(203) 322-cuts
www.haircutaly.com

OFF-CENTER BARBER SHOP
259 Sound Beach Avenue
Old Greenwich, CT 06870
(203) 637-1313

SHARKEY'S CUTS FOR KIDS
220 East Putnam Avenue
Cos Cob, CT 06807
(203) 629-KIDS (5437)
www.sharkeyscutsforkids.com
Good cuts for children, and they also offer "Glamour" birthday parties for girls (see chapter 6).

SUBWAY BARBER
315 Greenwich Avenue
Greenwich, CT 06830
(203) 869-3263
An institution in Greenwich, these barbers are great with kids! Haircuts for boys and girls are $15.

VILLAGE BARBER
238 Sound Beach Avenue
Old Greenwich, CT 06870
(203) 637-1161
Like Subway Barber, this is a classic barber shop—with the exception of the little cars for kids to sit in while they're getting their hair cut.

FINE PHOTOGRAPHY

You'll definitely want to capture memories of your child at various stages of his/her life as the years go by. Here are the popular photographers in town who specialize in children's portraits:

ACTION ARTS PHOTOGRAPHY
242 Soundbeach Avenue
Old Greenwich, CT 06870
(203) 637-2685
www.actionartsphotography.com

CHI CHI UBINA
(203) 698-1784
www.chichiubina.com
chichi@chichiubina.com

CLASSIC KIDS, GREENWICH
Kathleen Miller
54 Greenwich Avenue
Greenwich, CT 06830
(203) 622-2358
www.classickidsphotography.com
Fairly new to Greenwich, Classic Kids Photography creates unique, fun, and lasting portraits of children and families. They specialize in archival black-and-white and hand-painted photographs, which lend an heirloom look to portraits of your kids.

JEFFREY SHAW PHOTOGRAPHY
39 Lewis Street
Greenwich, CT 06830
(203) 622-4838
Selecting a photographer is a very personal decision based on the style that one wants. We have used Jeffrey Shaw on several occasions for our family and holiday pictures and really like his photographs.

As a matter of fact, he took the picture on the back of this book! Jeffrey Shaw really manages to capture everyone's personality.

STUDIO A PHOTOGRAPHY
418 East Putnam Avenue
Cos Cob, CT 06807
(203) 661-3393

BARGAIN SHOPPING

Greenwich Avenue abounds in clothing stores for adults and children. You'll find adorable children's clothing in all of the stores noted here. Every year in July, most towns in the Greenwich area have **SIDEWALK SALES**.

In addition, two factory outlets, **CLINTON CROSSINGS** and **WOODBURY COMMONS**, about an hour's drive from Greenwich, have quite a few stores for children and offer factory prices. However, chose a good time of day to go—the crowds can be overwhelming.

A good place for bargains is **MARSHALL'S**, located in the Ridgeway Shopping Center, off Summer Street in Stamford. **OLD NAVY** and **CARTER'S** are located in the same strip mall and are also good places to shop for basics.

Chapter 9

FURNITURE & SUPPLIES

Before I had my first child, I went a little crazy making lists and doing extensive research on all the things I needed for the new baby. Well before the baby's arrival, I ran out and purchased among many things, a bouncy seat, etc., etc. Then I was given a baby shower and what did I receive as a gift but a bouncy seat, which meant I had to return the one I'd already bought. Later, after my daughter was born, I found out that she couldn't stand being in the bouncy seat! So, lesson learned: Wait. Buy only the essentials before your baby is born.

When you go into any baby furniture/equipment store it's overwhelming to see the number of things manufacturers have come up with for babies. It takes a while to separate what you don't really need from what you actually do need, so take your time, especially if this is your first child. Go to a few stores and see what is available before making any final decisions. Here is my list of the essential items:

PORTABLE CRIB/PLAY-YARD - People may recommend getting a bassinet (it is a beautiful piece of furniture, after all) but you really won't use it for very long. It's a lot more useful to get a portable crib/play-yard, such as a Pack 'n' Play, which can double as a bassinet for the first month or two. Not only is it lightweight and therefore easy to move around the house, but you can also travel easily with one. And, when the baby has grown out of the bassinet stage, you can use it as a small playpen while you take a shower!

CRIB - No dearth of choices when purchasing a crib! Your choice will probably depend on furniture style, but there are two features you should look for: ability to adjust the height of the mattress (initially, you'll want it near the top and later you'll want it toward the bottom so your toddler can't act on his/her wild desire to jump out of the crib); and the ease with which the crib's sides can be lowered (you don't want to be fumbling with the latch in the middle of the night).

CHANGING TABLE - Get a dressing table with a flip top on which you put a pad to change your baby. As your baby gets older, you can get rid of the flip top and keep the dressing table. It's also useful to have drawers nearby—you can use them to store creams, diapers, undershirts, etc., so you don't have to run to a closet or separate area to get these items. You'll be amazed at how quickly a little squirmy baby can wiggle out of the latch.

ROCKING CHAIR/GLIDER - At first I thought I would never need a rocking chair (also known as a glider) but I ended up spending many an hour in one feeding a baby, burping a baby, consoling an upset child. This is definitely a worthwhile investment.

CAR SEAT - You'll go through a variety of car seats. First you'll need an infant car seat, which faces the rear of the car and is good for babies up to 20 lbs. After your baby reaches

20lbs., you need a toddler car seat. Later, when your child is about 4–5, he/she will be able to move on to a booster seat.

STROLLER - If you lived in the city, you'd want a fancy, well-built stroller because you do a lot of walking. In Greenwich, get a Snap 'n Go stroller: your car seat attaches to it, which makes it a lot easier to get your child in and out of you car. As your child gets older, I recommend an umbrella stroller. The key word at this stage is lightweight: find something that collapses easily that you can carry into and out of your car without breaking your back. I am a big fan of MacLaren umbrella strollers because they are extremely durable, fold and unfold easily, and are lightweight.

BOUNCY SEAT - The simpler the better. My kids didn't like the fancy bouncy seats with all those "soothing" vibrations! But this is entirely a matter of personal preference. Get one that can be moved from one room to another easily so go for bouncy seat that is lightweight.

HIGH CHAIR - This can be purchased later—you'll only begin to use it after the baby is 3 months old. Some things to bear in mind while shopping for a high chair: how easy it is to remove the tray table (a very important feature—you'll be amazed at the stuff that gets inside the crevices of the chair); how easy it is to lower and raise the seat; number of straps—the tray table alone is not enough to keep your child in the seat so you need straps, especially as you child gets older.

BABY CARRIER - For walking around town or your neighborhood, you may want to get a baby carrier or sling. Try to borrow one from a friend, since you probably won't use it for a long time. I remember using the Baby Bjorn a lot with my first child, who was a bit colicky. At about 5:30 each evening, she would start crying inconsolably. So, I'd put her in the baby carrier and start ironing – the movement and the heat soothed her. For a while...

THE SWING - Some kids love the swing and others hate it. Before going out and buying one try to borrow one, or try one out at a friend's house to see whether your child enjoys it.

BABY MONITOR - This is important, especially at night, to let you hear your baby when he/she is in another room. It's kind of a shock to find out how much you don't hear when you're sleep-deprived! So you need that monitor.

BELLINI BABY AND TEEN FURNITURE
984 High Ridge Road
Stamford, CT 06905
(203) 703-2084
Let's just say that Bellini's is the Tiffany's of baby stores... Need I say more?

BUY BUY BABY
1019 Central Park Avenue
Scarsdale, NY 10583
(914) 725-9220
This superstore has everything you could possibly want for a baby or older child, at reasonable prices.

GLORIA'S KIDS BEDS
1930 West Main Street
Stamford, CT
(800) 600-KIDS

GO TO YOUR ROOM
234 Mill Street
Greenwich, CT 06830
(203) 532-9701

KID'S HOME FURNISHING
11 Forest Street
Stamford, CT 06901
(203) 327-1333

KID'S SUPPLY CO.
14 Railroad Avenue
Greenwich, CT 06830
(203) 422-2100

THE RIGHT START
42 West Putnam Avenue
Greenwich, CT 06830
(203) 422-2525

TOYS 'R' US
59 Connecticut Avenue
Norwalk, CT 06850
(203) 852-7103
The well-known superstore Toys 'R' Us has all kinds of furniture as well as toys for children. The furniture is not always the best quality, but it's fine for the basics, such as bouncy seats or portable cribs/play-yards.

You can also find children's toys, clothing and other necessities at these area superstores:

STAMFORD TARGET
21 Broad Street
Stamford, CT 06901
(203) 388-0006

WHITE PLAINS TARGET
9 City Place
White Plains, NY 10601
(914) 821-0012

KMART
399 Tarrytown Road
White Plains, NY 10607
(914) 684-1184

COSTCO
1 Westchester Avenue
Port Chester, NY 10573
(914) 935-3100
or
779 Connecticut Avenue
Norwalk, CT 06854
(203) 822-2000

BABY-PROOFERS

Before your child starts to crawl, you'll have to start thinking about baby-proofing your home. An excellent website, www.babyproofingdirectory.com, is a comprehensive source of information on baby-proofing, including tips, equipment, and local baby-proofing services. In the Greenwich area we have:

CHILD PROOFERS
540 West Boston Post Road
Mamaroneck, NY 10543
(914) 381-5106

PEEK-A-BOO BABYPROOFING
6 Old King's Highway
Wilton, CT 06897
(203) 322-8488

NOTES

Chapter 10

RESTAURANTS

Most restaurants in Greenwich, even some of the fancier ones, are very accepting when it comes to very young diners. The restaurants listed here are bound to please both parents and children.

TAKE THE KIDS

ABIS
Japanese
381 Greenwich Avenue
Greenwich, CT 06830
(203) 862-9100
Abis is one of my family's favorite places to go for birthday celebrations. The hibachi (we call it "the cook-in-front-of-you" place) is a hit with children of all ages. For birthdays, the staff will sing a special birthday song and take a Polaroid picture of the family – it's very cute!

ARMONK BAGEL EMPORIUM
Bagels
391 Main Street
Armonk, NY 10504
(914) 273-9111

BEACHHOUSE CAFÉ
American
220 Sound Beach Avenue
Old Greenwich, CT 06870
(203) 637-0367

BELLA NONNA FAMILY RESTAURANT
Italian
371 East Putnam Avenue
Greenwich, CT 06807
(203) 869-4445

BOXCAR CANTINA
Mexican
44 Old Field Point Road
Greenwich, CT 06830
(203) 661-4774

CENTRO AT THE MILL
American
328 Pemberwick Road
Greenwich, CT 06831
(203) 531-5514

CITY LIMITS DINER
American
132 Harvard Avenue
Stamford, CT 06902
(203) 348-7000

COSI
129 West Putnam Avenue
Greenwich, CT 06830
(203) 861-2674
I hear they have the best 'smores!

GARDEN CATERING
177 Hamilton Avenue
Greenwich CT 06830
(203) 422-2555
and
185 1/2 Sound Beach Avenue
Old Greenwich CT 06870
(203) 637-7699
www.gardencatering.net

KU
Japanese
85 East Putnam Avenue
Cos Cob, CT 06807
(203) 422-6310

MACKENZIE'S GRILL ROOM
American
148 Sound Beach Avenue
Old Greenwich, CT 06870
(203) 698-0223

MELI-MELO
French/Crepes
362 Greenwich Avenue
Greenwich, CT 06830
(203) 629-6153
Meli-Melo is a cute creperie on Greenwich Avenue. The crepes are delicious! The only drawback is that it is very small.

MY FAVORITE PLACE
1 Strickland Road
Cos Cob, CT 06807
(203) 869-1500
Opened by Greenwich High School graduates, My Favorite Place has a good menu for children and good salads for adults.

THE PIZZA FACTORY
Italian
380 Greenwich Avenue
Greenwich, CT 06830
(203) 661-5188
The Pizza Factory is a cute pizza place which makes delicious pizzas. Our favorite is the personal pizza.

Q
112 North Main Street
Port Chester, NY 10573
(914) 933-7427
Best barbecue ribs, chicken, brisket and pulled pork!
The owners of Q also own THE KNEADED BREAD in Port Chester, which sells the most amazing cakes, breads, pastries and soups. We love to take the kids there for breakfast!

THE KNEADED BREAD
181 North Main Street
Port Chester, NY 10573
(914) 937-9489

ROUTE 22 AMERICAN RESTAURANT AND BAR
American
55 Old Route 22
Armonk, NY 10504
(914) 765-0022
Route 22 is situated in a former 1930s gas station and they've retained the nostalgic ambiance. But the main attraction for kids are the games and the cars that their food comes in. Route 22 also has donut-making birthday parties for children. Needless to say, this place is so child-friendly that you can rule it out as a choice for a quiet, romantic evening with your spouse!

SUNDOWN SALOON
American
403 Greenwich Avenue
Greenwich, CT 06830
(203) 629-8212

TOP DOG
118 River Road
Cos Cob, CT 06807
(203) 661-0573

UPPER CRUST BAGEL CO.
Bagels
197 Sound Beach Avenue
Old Greenwich, CT 06870
(203) 698-0079

SNACKS & TREATS

ADA'S VARIETY SHOP
112 Riverside Avenue
Riverside, CT 06878
(203) 637-0305

ARCADIA COFFEE SHOP
20 Arcadia Road
Old Greenwich, CT 06870
(203) 637-8766

COLDSTONE CREAMERY
78 East Putnam Avenue
Greenwich, CT 06830
(203) 302-3300

DARLENE'S HEAVENLY DESIRES
185 Sound Beach Avenue
Old Greenwich, CT 06870
(203) 698-9441

GOFER ICE CREAM
522 East Putnam Avenue
Greenwich, CT 06830
(203) 661-9080

THE DRAWING ROOM
5 Suburban Avenue
Cos Cob, CT 06807
(203) 661-3737
www.thedrawingroom.com
This is a really cute tearoom in Cos Cob. It's a great place to take the kids for a snack or treat in the afternoon. Their hot chocolate is delicious. There is a nice design store adjacent to the tearoom too.

TAKEOUT FAVORITES

ARCURI'S PIZZA AND SALADS
226 East Putnam Avenue
Cos Cob, CT 06807
(203) 869-6999

BROADWAY NORTH PIZZA AND RESTAURANT
393 Main Street
Armonk, NY 10504
(914) 273-2234

GARDEN CATERING
185 1/2 Sound Beach Avenue
Old Greenwich, CT 06870
(203) 637-8271
and
177 Hamilton Avenue
Greenwich, Ct 06830
(203) 422-2255

GREENWICH PIZZA
356 West Putnam Avenue
Greenwich, CT 06830
(203) 622-8111

HUNAN CAFÉ
1233 East Putnam Avenue
Riverside, CT 06878
(203) 637-4341

HUNAN GOURMET
68 East Putnam Avenue
Greenwich, CT 06830
(203) 869-1940

LITTLE THAI KITCHEN
21 Saint Roche Avenue
Greenwich, CT 06830
(203) 622-2972

PENANG GRILL
55 Lewis Street
Greenwich, CT 06830
(203) 861-1988

PLANET PIZZA
28 Railroad Avenue
Greenwich, CT 06830
(203) 622-0999

POMODORO
1247 East Putnam Avenue
Greenwich, CT 06830
(203) 698-7779

SOUND BEACH PIZZA & GRILL
187 Sound Beach Avenue
Old Greenwich, CT 06870
(203) 637-1085

NOTES

Chapter 11

JUST FOR MOM

Okay, we've devoted eleven chapters of this book to showing you how to keep your kids happy. But now let's pay some attention to you, who makes it all possible. In those odd moments during the week—or the month—that you find yourself with an hour or two to spare, make an effort to treat yourself. Greenwich offers plenty of places to do it.

DAY SPAS

EMPY'S DAY SPA
138 Hamilton Avenue
Greenwich, CT 06830
(203) 661-6625
This is my favorite place for manicures and pedicures.

THE LOTUS WELLNESS CENTER
46 Pemberwick Road
Greenwich, CT 06831
(203) 531-4784
Robin Spiegel

NOELLE SPA FOR BEAUTY AND WELLNESS
1100 High Ridge Road
Stamford, CT 06905
(203) 322-3445

PARTNERS SALON & SPA
1200 East Putnam Avenue
Riverside, CT 06878
(203)637-0478

SERENITY SPA
116 East Putnam Avenue
Greenwich, CT 06830
(203) 629-9000

STONEWATER SPA
151 Greenwich Avenue
Greenwich, CT 06830
(203) 622-7424

WORKING IT OUT

THE FITNESS EDGE
1333 East Putnam Avenue
Greenwich, CT 06830
www.fitnessedge.net

GLOW YOGA
East Putnam Avenue
Riverside, CT 06878
This is a new yoga center opening
in April 2006 above Aux Delices in
Riverside.

GREENWICH YOGA
328 Pemberwick Road
Greenwich, CT 06831
(203) 532-0660
www.greenwichyoga.com
I started going to Yoga Samadhi
shortly after the studio first opened.
They offer a wide variety of classes
for people with different skills and
interests. The instructors are all
really good and the overall
atmosphere is warm and friendly.

THE KNEADED TOUCH IN FITNESS
83 Harvard Avenue
Stamford, CT 06902
(203) 967-1121
www.kneadedtouch.com
The Kneaded Touch specializes in
personal training and physical
therapy. I've seen the results—
several friends of mine have whole
new amazing bodies!

NEW YORK SPORTS CLUB
6 Liberty Way
Greenwich, CT 06830
(203) 869-1253

PEAK PHYSIQUE
50 Holly Hill Lane
Greenwich, CT 06830
(203)625-9595
www.peakphysique.biz
Specializes in personal training
but also offers Pilates, yoga,
and other classes.

SPORTSPLEX
49 Brownhouse Road
Stamford, CT
(203) 358-0066
www.sportsplex-ct.com

YOGA CENTER
125 Greenwich Avenue
Greenwich, CT 06830
(203) 661-0092

MEJO WIGGIN, LLC.
Central Greenwich
(203)629-3743
www.mejowiggin.com
Certifying Pilates Center

And, of course, there's the **YMCA**
and the **YWCA**, with gym facilities,
swimming pools, and aerobic classes.
The advantage of both of these places
is they have child care facilities on
the premises, so you can work out
while the kids are safe and cared for.

GREENWICH YWCA
259 East Putnam Avenue
Greenwich, CT 06830
(203) 869-6501
www.ywcagreenwich.org

GREENWICH YMCA
50 East Putnam Avenue
Greenwich, CT 06830
(203) 869-1630
www.gwymca.org

BACK TO YOUR ROOTS
LAURA PARISI
2 Arbor Lane
Old Greenwich, Ct 06870
(203) 698-0473
LParisi55@aol.com
Holistic health counseling, whole
foods cooking workshops and market
tours for busy mothers and families
who want to be vibrantly healthy.

MIND EXPANSION

COS COB LIBRARY BOOK CLUB
Cos Cob Library
This book club meets the first
Thursday night of the month at
7:30 PM.

GREENWICH DEPARTMENT OF
CONTINUING EDUCATION
290 Greenwich Avenue
Greenwich, CT 06830
(203) 625-7474
(203) 625-7477
www.greenwichschools.org/gce
Offers a wide variety of classes and
workshops for adults.

GREENWICH CLASSIC FILM SERIES
at the Crown Plaza Movie Theater on
Railroad Avenue screens movies from
the 30s to the 70s.
CLASSIC FILM SERIES INC.
15 East Putnam Avenue, Suite 175
Greenwich, CT 06830
(914) 725-0099

GREENWICH LIBRARY
101 West Putnam Avenue
Greenwich, CT 06830
(203) 622-7900
www.greenwichlibrary.org
Greenwich Library has a wide variety
of programs for adults, such as the
Foreign Affairs Book Club, **Science
Fiction Book Club**, the **Friday Film
Series** and the **Library Lecture Series**.

JEWISH FICTION BOOK CLUB
Led by Rabbi Chapin of the Greenwich
Reform Temple, this book club meets
every month at the Arcadia Coffee Co.
at 7:00 PM.

JUST BOOKS BOOK CLUB
28 Arcadia Road
Old Greenwich, CT 06870
203-637-0707
bookshop@justbooks.org
This group meets the second Thursday
night of the month at 7:00 PM.

NORWALK COMMUNITY COLLEGE
188 Richards Avenue
Norwalk, CT 06854
(203) 857-7000
www.nctc.commnet.edu
Many classes on many subjects,
day and evening.

PURCHASE COLLEGE
735 Anderson Hill Road
Purchase, NY 10577
Tel. (914) 251-6500
www.purchase.edu/ce
Purchase College, part of the
State University of New York system,
offers an array of non-credit courses,
primarily in the arts. Regular courses
are also available at a non-credit
level.

GIFTS FOR MOMS

I think that the best gifts for moms are time and sleep. I have to admit that I would rather have a "day off" to sleep in, to hang out with friends, or to just read a book. When I had my fourth child, I got two absolutely great gifts: the first was a "certificate" for home-delivered meals; and for the second gift, my friend took my older children for an afternoon playdate so that I could spend some time alone with the baby. Both of these were truly wonderful!

For some gift ideas, for yourself or friends, the following are some of my favorites:

ROMERO DESIGNS
254 Mill Street
Greenwich, CT 06830
(203) 531-5265
www.romerodesigns.com
Tami Romero creates unique jewelry using photographs of children or family. I have gotten my husband all sorts of cool cufflinks, and a variety of key chains for the grandparents.

BEADS IN THE LOFT
3 Lewis Street
Greenwich, CT 06830
(203) 861-0086
I just love all of Jenni Freedman's pieces – they are really beautiful!

HOAGLAND'S
175 Greenwich Avenue
Greenwich, CT 06830
(203) 869-2127
Hoagland's is always a safe bet for gifts.

SEA CLOTH
107 Greenwich Avenue
Greenwich, CT 06830
(203) 422-6150
Sea Cloth has a lot of fun accessories and items for the home.

For a friend's 40th Birthday, several of us went to a cooking class. We did more chatting than cooking but it was a lot of fun! In addition to **Aux Delices**, another place one can take cooking classes is with **Time to Eat** at **Christopher Peacock Cabinetry**. For information, call Nicole Straight at (203) 221-8306 or visit www.time-to-eat.com

NOTES

NOTES

NOTES

A Guide to Greenwich for Kids